A Donner Party Story:
Daughters of Destiny

Enjoy,
Frankye Craig

Frankye Craig

A Donner Party Story:

Daughters of Destiny

Published by Frankye Craig, Reno, Nevada

www.donnerpartyhistory.com

Copyright © 2007, Frankye Craig
ISBN-13: 978-0-9794904-0-8
ISBN-10: 0-9794904-0-5

Cover Illustration: Diana Monfalcone
Interior Design and Production: Frankye Craig
1st Printing: June 2007

Forward

When you place the Donner Party in the context of the total story of the emigration of 1846, they are a small and insignificant part. They were no different than the thousands of other emigrants that traveled the trail in the mid-1840's. That they had extraordinary bad luck was the greatest factor in their awful tragedy, but faced with uncertainty, back-breaking labor, and fear—fear of running out of food, of not making it over the mountains—some of the social fabric of the group shredded. But the story has, in the words of George Stewart, "the scarlet thread of courage and the golden thread of heroism."

The narrator for this Donner Party story is Eliza Donner, the youngest daughter of wagon train captain George Donner and his wife Tamsen. The narration has been dramatized for interest with concern for historical accuracy.

There were many diaries, reports and letters written by people who traveled with the Donner and Reed families on the trail in 1846 and many other accounts written or told by the survivors themselves. I have used those materials for the history. A list of the resources used is in the back of the book.

Frankye Craig

Contents

Sometimes sorrows come to us; they cannot be prevented. Our family, and the other families that were with us, experienced the worst of sorrows that can come to man. Children usually escape terrible times that trouble their parents, catching only a sense that things are not right. But alas, we children could not escape these woes, we had to live through them.

My name is Eliza Donner, and this is my story. My hope is that it will touch your heart, that you might have an understanding of the people who undertook a long-ago journey and faced a terrible ordeal in the mountains of California. Those people were the members of what has become known as the Donner Party.

Chapter One

It was a crisp spring day in April of 1846 when we left our home in Springfield, Illinois.

We children were full of excitement as we waited on the front porch with Mother while the last team of oxen were being gathered and put into their yokes. We could hear Father and Noah yelling at them. They bellowed and jumped around the yard, kicking up a lot of dust and knocking things over. Finally the task was accomplished and Father came to us, knocking the dust off his pants with his hat.

Mother turned and started into the house. "George, I've had to leave so much that is dear to me, I will not leave my rocking chair too. I just won't."

"Tamsen, there's no room for it!" Father exclaimed. "I've gone along with all the other stuff, the heavy books an' all—"

"The chair has to go with us, or I'm going to sit in it and wave good-bye as you go through the gate!"

Father shook his head in annoyance but brought the chair from the house.

"Move the beddin' and see if you can get this in there," he said to Noah. Noah James was one of our hired men. "We'll have to take the damn thing out ever' time we need to get in the wagon!"

We giggled. Mother didn't like swear words and reprimanded anyone who used them, including Father. Father whistled at our other hired men, Jim Smith and Hiram Miller, and motioned for them to start the wagons moving. Also going along was John Denton, who had immigrated from England.

There were five children in our family: Elitha, Leanna, Frances, Georgeanna, and myself, Eliza, the youngest. Our parents were George and Tamsen Donner. We had three wagons, two wagons carried the supplies and household items that we would need for the long journey, and the third wagon all the goods that Father would trade for land in California.

Father turned towards the house and called out to Mother. "Mother! What in blazes are you doin' now?"

Mother came from the house carrying the tin box in which she kept important papers and little treasures. She looked stricken, her eyes red and puffy. Father placed his arm around her shoulders.

"Honey, I know it's hard to leave, but we need to think ahead to the new life in California."

"Yes, I know. It's just last minute jitters. Go ahead, girls, get in the wagon."

My sisters and I clambered up and Mother handed the box to me to hold while she stepped up into the wagon. The wagons began to move, creaking and groaning as they met the rough ground of the road.

I had been excited to leave, but now sadness clutched at my heart. The comfortable old house would not have our family to warm and protect ever again. We would never laugh and play in the big barn, nor would we again taste of the fruit from our orchard. We passed the big field where Father had raised his horses and new tears coursed down my cheeks. I looked at Mother and she tried to smile, but I could see that she was crying too.

It was scary to contemplate, this journey to California. After leaving the Missouri Territory we would find rare vestige of civilization for hundreds and hundreds of miles, and that would only be crude trader's forts, peopled by a few white men who were half-savage themselves. The route was a new one and there would be no marked road after we left the trail to the Oregon Territory, and then we would travel across a thousand miles of mostly unknown wilderness. But Father was used to journeying from place to place, his family had moved westward from

North Carolina in stages—Kentucky, Indiana, Texas, and then Illinois. Father had no apprehensions about this journey to California.

After we had gone about a mile, we could see other wagons ahead of us. It was the wagons of Father's brother, Jacob Donner. Jacob and his wife, Betsey, had seven children: Solomon, William, George Jr., Mary, Isaac, Samuel, and Lewis.

We camped for the night in the village, which was about two and a half miles from our farm. Already in camp was the third family that would join our group, that of James and Margaret Reed. The Reeds had four children: Virginia, Patty, James Jr., and Thomas. With the Reed family was Mrs. Reed's mother, Sarah Keyes; Eliza Williams and her brother, Baylis, who were servants; and several hired men.

We jumped down from the wagon, anxious to run off to join our cousins and get a closer look at the Reed family wagon. It looked a lot different than ours.

"Children, don't run off."

"Mother, their wagon has a door on the side. Like a stagecoach," said Frances.

"And it's bigger than ours, really big," said Georgia. "Can we go see?"

"Yes, in a few minutes, but first we must wash up and change our dresses. Frances, I must braid your hair again. Please, girls, get in the wagon."

"Mother, we ain't dirty."

"Frances, we do not say ain't, it is not proper language."

"Everybody does, Mother."

"We do not. I will explain it to you again. It is not that using ain't, or a curse word, for that matter, is a mortal sin, but people who do use words like that show that they are uneducated, and do not have enough command of language to use more suitable words. Come, Georgeanna, Eliza, you must change your dresses. Then we will go see the wagon."

Mr. and Mrs. Reed were standing beside their wagon.

"Tamsen, I want to show you inside. Mr. Reed has done marvelous work to make it nice," said Mrs. Reed.

Mr. Reed fingered his mustache and looked proud. "I can assure you that it is the most comfortable wagon that has ever headed west."

"Tamsen, please come in and say hello to Mother," said Mrs. Reed.

My sisters and I started to follow Mother, but Mrs. Reed held out her hand.

"Children, perhaps you can see the wagon another time."

Mother turned and looked at us sympathetically. She knew how we anticipated seeing the inside of the wagon. "Children, go find your cousins. I have planned a special treat for all of you. I'll be along shortly."

Later, as we sat around the fire nibbling on the cookies that Mother had for us, she told of her visit to the Reed wagon.

"It was very nice. When one enters it is like stepping into a small parlor. On each side are bench seats, and under the seats are storage compartments. The sides of the wagon were built out over the wheels so that beds could be put across the wagon on each end. And there's even a small stove."

"A stove inside the wagon? It'll smoke 'em out or burn up the cover!" exclaimed Aunt Betsey.

"No, it was well thought out. Mr. Reed passed the smoke pipe through the top and made a metal ring to keep the canvas from catching fire." Mother paused and frowned. "I feel sorry for Mrs. Keyes. I fear she has not long to live and the journey will be hard on her. The consumption is very bad."

The evening was a festive one. Many people came to the campground to visit us, bringing dishes and kettles of food to share. Everyone was sad to think that we might never see each other again.

The morning brought a sky heavy with the threat of rain and mists were clinging to the hollows and streams as we began our journey. It was a cacophony of noise and a hubbub of activity—oxen, horses, dogs, children, all moving in different directions. The women darted around putting gear away, the men shouting and cursing as they struggled to put the oxen in the yokes.

At last the lead wagon jerked forward, its white canvas top swaying as the wheels rolled over deep ruts in the road. The rest fell in behind, the loose stock bringing up the rear. It was quite a caravan.

During this part of the journey the men trained the oxen to the yoke and to respond to commands. The women learned to cook over fires on the ground. Mother and Aunt Betsey had the hems of several skirts burned from the fire and they soon cut their dresses shorter, which shocked Mrs. Reed because their ankles showed.

We traveled across Illinois and Missouri towards the village of Independence, where many emigrants were gathering. All had gone smoothly and we enjoyed the journey immensely. In the evenings when camp was made we would have merry talk and singing. It was Elitha and Leanna's duty to keep us little ones quiet and entertained, and we would play Button, Button, and other hand games.

One day Leanna noticed some gnats flying around the rising bread dough and lifted the cloth that covered the pan. "Mother! The bread dough is covered with gnats. It's black with them. Yuck!"

The dough was ruined. Mother tossed it into the bushes, where a fight broke out between the dogs to see which would own it. One of our dogs must have got some of the bread dough—he was upchucking all night under the wagon.

It was that same dog that caused trouble with our ox, Buster. The dog had a perverse attachment to teasing the ox, nipping at his heels, neck and ears when the ox was yoked to the wagon. Buster would try to retaliate, but restrained by the yoke, he would only cause a disruption in the progress of the team. Noah would whack him with his whip to get him settled again. The ox tried to keep an eye on the dog, who would retreat, grinning from ear to ear, waiting for the next opportunity to repeat the torment.

One day after the noon stop when Buster was being led to the yokes, he spied his tormenter lying asleep on a pile of hay, limp in relaxation, lips twitching as a dream flitted through his head. With a massive bellow, Buster lunged for the dog, flipping him in the air with his horns several times before the dog managed to crawl under the wagon, more dead than alive.

"It serves him right," said Mother, "but I feel sorry for him, he's hurt so terribly. One leg is broken and I'm sure he has cracked ribs too."

Mother put the dog in a sling under the wagon, where he lay for days, yipping with every jolt. Buster would snort in derision whenever he was led past the wagon.

The dog recovered but stayed well away from the oxen when the wagons rolled and crawled into his sling when the oxen were free from the yokes.

We crossed many creeks, streams and rivers. Many times the wagons bogged down in deep mud and double-teaming was necessary to extricate them. We would ride in the wagon if the weather was unpleasant, but usually we would walk. The older children would ride on the horses and found it exciting to scare up wolves, deer, and wild game as we moved through the countryside.

After a month of travel, we reached our jumping-off place, the hamlet of Independence, Missouri.

Chapter Two

Independence was crowded with people and wagons. Many were forming up into companies.

The men folk avidly perused the newspapers for the latest information on the pending emigration, and visited around, inspecting and appraising the various wagons, teams, and equipment. They endlessly discussed the business of journeying across the country. Several of the men who visited our camp thought that Mr. Reed's wagon was too heavy for such a journey.

We three little ones, watched over by our older sisters and our cousin, Solomon, perched on a big log as we took it all in. We noticed a group of people gathered around a grizzled old mountaineer squatting down next to the wheel of a wagon.

"Look," whispered Solomon, "that's the old mountaineer, Zeb. He came to a meetin' we had back to home. Let's get closer, I want to hear what he's saying."

Zeb was clad in blackened and greasy buckskin leather, with rows of beading and fringing on his shirt and trousers. Indian adornments dangled from his neck. His voice was raspy. "Most a' my life I been in the mount'ins trappin' an' huntin' beaver." He looked at one and then another with faded blue eyes. "I done fit Injuns dozens a' times, still got an arrer head or two whar they got me. I done lost my outfit two, three times from bein' attacked by the varmints. The Blackfeet are the worst, by damn. I hate them Blackfeet, an' the Crows are bad too."

Zeb wiped his mouth on his sleeve, took his knife out and began stabbing the ground with it.

"The beaver business, it don't shine no more," he said, spitting out his chaw and wiping his mouth again. "It's through. Gone. Now the thing is Oregon an' California, guidin' greenhorns out to the new lands." He jerked his thumb toward the wagon behind him. "I'm headin' west myself, guidin' this here wagon party out to the Oregon Territory."

"Do you know much of California?"

Zeb put one foot on a stump, crossing his arms over his upraised leg. "I think it's a good land. Thar's no winter an' anythin' kin grow all year. Th'ar ain't many people, mostly Mexicans. Thar's land fer the takin', an' soon she'll be United States territory."

"What's your opinion of the best way to go to California?"

"I'm of a mind that the Oregon Territory is the best place, but if'n yer needle's set on California, I allow it's the next best." Zeb paused to spit. For him spitting was not a neat affair and as a result his beard and the front of his buckskin shirt had a dirty brown stain down the center.

"How to get thar?" Zeb squeezed his eyes into little slits and slowly scratched his beard while he contemplated the question.

"Well, ye head north to the Platte River an' foller it west to the Shining Mountains. Then ye go along the Sweetwater to Bridger's tradin' post. 'Course, you could take Sublette's cut-off just shy of Bridger's if'n ye wanted to an' didn't need supplies. It'll take ye to Fort Hall a little shorter."

Zeb took his foot off the stump, picked up a stick and drew lines in the dirt. "See here, from both places ye can go north to Fort Hall." He stabbed a point in the dirt and drew a long line. "From there, it's west, then south down to Ogden's River. Foller on 'til the river ends in a sink an' then keep on west 'til ye gits to high mount'ins. They'll be higher than anythin' ye seen so far. After the last of those mount'ins ye'll find the holdin's of Mr. Sutter. New Helvetia, he calls it. I've heard he's mighty fine to Americans."

Zeb began cleaning his fingernails with his knife. As the crowd began to move away, he called out. "Mind ye now, ye don't want ter git to the high mountains late in the season 'cause the passes close with snow. Ye could be trapped fer the winter."

That evening at the campfire the grown-ups talked about the day's events. Solomon was squatting down by the fire, stabbing the ground with a big knife. He got up and moved to sit beside Father.

"Uncle George, I asked Zeb 'bout a way to get to the Salt Lake without havin' to go by Fort Hall. He said he'd never heard of a way to go with wagons, an' he should know, bein' a mountain man an' all. He says we'll have trouble with Injuns too."

Our ears perked up. Indians! We'd heard stories about how Indians would attack and kill people and steal their animals. Mr. Reed frowned at Solomon.

"The Indians we'll encounter are peaceably inclined. They'll pilfer whatever they can, but if we are in a good-sized company we won't have any trouble. We do need to join up with a good group before we get into the Indian country."

"Yeah, but Zeb said …"

Aunt Betsey glared at Solly. "You stop that, y'hear? You'll scare the little ones."

We'd already been scared by all the stories we'd heard. Patty Reed had related to us some of the stories her grandmother had told her.

"They would sneak up on anyone out alone and cleave their heads with a tomahawk. They would attack houses and burn them, making the people run out, only to be killed. My grandma's auntie was taken prisoner by the savages and was captive for *five years*."

Mother sat down that evening and wrote a letter to her sister, our Auntie Poor.

May 11, 1846
My dear sister,

I commenced writing to you some months ago, but the letter was laid aside to be finished the next day & was never touched. A nice sheet of pink letter paper was taken out & has got so much soiled that it cannot be written upon. Now in the midst of preparation for starting across the mountains I am seated on the grass in the midst of the tent to say a few words to my dearest only sister. One would suppose that I loved her but little or I should have not neglected her so long, but I have heard from you by Mr. Greenleaf & every month have intended to write.

My three daughters are round me, one at my side trying to sew. Georgeanna fixing herself up in an old India rubber cap & Eliza knocking on my paper asking me ever so many questions. They often talk to me of Aunty Poor. I can give you no idea of the hurry of this place at this time. It is supposed there be 700 wagons start from this place, this season. We go to California, to the bay of Francisco. It is a four months trip. We have three wagons furnished with food & clothing etc., drawn by three yoke of oxen each. We take cows along & milk them & have some butter though not as much as we would like.

I am willing to go & have no doubt it will be an advantage to our children & to us. I came here last evening & start tomorrow morning on the long journey.

Wm's family was well when I left Springfield. He will write to you soon as he finds another home. He says he has received no answer to his two last letters, is about to start to Wisconsin as he considers Illinois unhealthy.

Farewell my sister, you shall hear from me as soon as I have an opportunity. Love to Mr. Poor, the children & all friends.
T. E. Donner

In the morning our group of wagons moved out, following the deep ruts of the Santa Fe Trail. As we left the campground we saw a brilliant rainbow arching in the sky, but soon clouds closed in and the sky became overcast and very gray.

That afternoon rain fell heavily, accompanied with loud peals of thunder and flashes of lightning. We climbed into the wagon, our noses tickling at the musty smell of the damp contents. Rain drummed against the canvas and the lantern swung crazily as gusts of wind rocked the wagon as if it were a boat on the high seas. Later the skies cleared, but Father decided to go no farther that day.

"The road is gonna be knee deep in mud tomorrow," said Father. "We should stop until things dry out. It's hard on the animals."

"That's a good idea, George," said Mr. Reed. "I'll go ahead and visit with groups to get a feel for the company we might want to join."

"Girls," said Mother, "I think I see a patch of prairie peas. Come, we'll walk a little, it will feel good after being cooped up all afternoon. I'm anxious to see what plants we will find in this new country. This is pink verbena, and that over there is wild indigo. So beautiful!"

Uncle Jacob was late joining us at the cooking fire the next morning for breakfast. "I didn't sleep hardly a wink with those damned dogs barking all night," he complained. He stretched and sat down on a log close to the fire, scratching his beard.

"Mother, Uncle Jacob said a curse word."

Uncle frowned and pointed his finger at Georgia. "Now, you just stick to yer knittin', little girl, an' don't be getting' yer mother on me."

We were in the middle of making breakfast when the wind began to blow, and rain came upon us with almost the darkness of night.

"Our bread ain't gonna cook through with the fire out, ain't been goin' long enough," said Aunt Betsey. "Ever'thin we have is wet through an' I cain't hardly walk with the mud stickin' to my feet in a ball. Our men're crazy to put us through this."

As we proceeded, the country rose into high rolling prairie almost destitute of timber. We met three returning Santa Fe traders driving a herd of mules.

"Those were the poorest mules I ever saw," said Uncle Jacob. "That man said the journey he'd just been on was a hard one, but that our journey will be even harder and would shorten our lives by ten years."

Father chuckled. "You think it's been that hard? Seems like we been on a continual picnic."

"I don't figure I got ten years no-how, so I guess it don't matter."

It continued to rain, saturating the ground even more. We reached a creek with steep banks and the men had to use ropes to lower the wagons and then pull them up the other side. In the afternoon, we crossed a stream called the Wakarusa and camped in a grove of big trees.

The land was covered with grass and rose and fell in ever-higher swells. The wagons moved slowly over hill and hollow and we could hear only the muttering of the wind, the creaking of the wagons, and on the breeze, snippets of talk and the "gee-haw" and "whoa-haw" of a teamster talking to the oxen. Leanna and Elitha, walking by the wagon, pointed to a rise ahead.

"Mother, look. Are those Indians?"

"Yes, don't be alarmed. They mean us no harm."

Some of the men in the group who were on horseback gathered at the front of the train as we neared the Indians, two men and two women with their children. The Indian mothers carried their babies on their backs in a blanket, only their little round faces showing, their black eyes staring out at us.

When we left camp one of our men threw away a pair of old boots, the soles of which were fastened with iron nails. Our Indian visitors eagerly seized upon the boots and in their language of signs and grunts, congratulated themselves upon becoming the possessors of such wealth.

We were stopped at the rain-swollen Kansas River. We had to use flat-boats poled by Indians to take the wagons across. Mother was nervous that the rafts might fall apart with our wagons.

"Tamsen, it's six miles to a fordin' place. We'll use the flat-boats."

May 18, 1846
My Dear Friend,
In compliance with my promise, I proceed to give you a hasty & brief account of our journey with the California emigration to this point. We crossed the Kansas River yesterday by placing the wagons on flat boats & swimming the horses and oxen. We expect to join the company headed by Colonel Russell by tomorrow at the latest, as they are waiting for us to come up with them at a place called Soldier Creek.

We heard the war news some twenty miles back from here, but the particulars we did not receive until last evening when Mr. Webb, of the Expositer newspaper, came through with mail. It has created no alarm in our camp nor in any other as far as can be ascertained, with most seeming to anticipate pleasure rather than otherwise in the conflict with the Mexicans when we arrive in California. Our party continues to enjoy the most robust health.
Mrs. George Donner

We caught up with the large company led by Mr. Russell and camped off to the side of the main group.

"I don't cotton to be in such a crowd," said Uncle Jacob. "It'll be hard to find forage for the animals, an' the dust raised by so many wagons'll be intolerable."

Father tossed the stick he'd been chewing on into the fire and got up. "We ain't got no choice. We need to be with a large group, we'll be gettin' into Indian country soon. An' they already voted to accept us."

"I heard there's thirteen wagons that're gonna split off tomorrow," said Uncle Jacob. "Mebbe we should join up with them."

"That right? Do you know the leader?"

"It's a group led by Mr. Gordon," said Mr. Reed. "I prefer the leadership of Mr. Russell."

"I agree," said Father. "We'll stay with his group. Will you go along with that, Jacob?"

"I reckon. There'll be more men to stand watch when we get into the Injun country."

The company stopped to observe the Sabbath and held church services. The minister talked on and on. We watched as most of the children began sneaking away and we looked at Mother but she frowned and shook her head. At last it was over.

"Girls, you must change your clothes, and then we will have dinner before you can play," said Mother.

Several families brought food and joined us at our wagons.

"Wasn't that an excellent message by the Reverend? I am so glad that this company keeps the Sabbath," trilled Mrs. Thornton.

"Seems like all that preacher can talk about," said Father, "is fire and brimstone. I don't see how a lovin' God could ever be mean enough to create a place like Hell. There's enough Hell on earth without there bein' any call for it in the hereafter."

Mrs. Thornton gasped. Mother nudged Father with her elbow. Mr. Bryant stood and put his empty plate into our washtub. "It's nice to observe the Sabbath but we're moving too slowly. It seems that many people are desirous of shortening each day's march, and when once encamped are reluctant to move. I'm fearful that winter will find us in the mountains of California, or that we will run short of provisions. I do not fear for myself, but for the women and children."

After dinner Mr. Russell and a group of people came to our camp to welcome us to the wagon train.

Mr. Russell stood on a wagon pole and addressed the group. "Y'all are part of Manifest Destiny, a part of history. Do not think of history as somethin' remote that concerns only kings, queens, an' generals. It concerns *you*."

He brought a flask to his mouth, drank from it, then wiped his chin with the back of his hand.

"You an' your families march across the pages of history. The farmer that plows a furrow is of more importance than the leader of an army. The army can destroy, the furrow can feed."

"I never could figure out what he was talkin' about," said Uncle Jacob after everyone left our camp.

"He's a real wind-bag," said Father.

"His point was that we who have left our homes to live in the new lands are pioneers," said Mother. "We're forging a road, so to speak, that many, many others will follow. All these people now on the road and all who will follow us into the Oregon and California territories will eventually cause these places to come under the dominion of the United States."

"That sounds like a tall order of business," said Father.

"It will happen," said Mr. Reed.

What had been perceived before as adventurous and exciting, now became a tedious and demanding journey. As we traveled, the country changed into ever higher hills, one rise flowing into another.

We had our first encounter with Indians in large numbers. They looked very wretched, their clothing dirty and in tatters. Some of the Indian men had shaved their heads except for a tuft from the forehead over the top of their scalp, like the comb of a rooster. We hovered by the wagon, clinging to Mother's skirts.

"Mother, what makes that noise when they walk?"

"They have some metal pieces attached to their clothes that jingle when they move. It's quite musical, isn't it?"

"I think we'd better make a strong guard around the camp tonight," said Mr. Reed. "If we don't, we might find ourselves short of some of our gear and livestock in the morning."

With the dawn the Indians were back, begging for food. The

women of the company gathered flour, bacon, and other things which were given to the chief to be shared with his people. We moved on through a pretty valley, on one side mound-shaped hills, on the other a creek.

"Look, girls, wild roses."

We little sisters gathered some in our aprons, but not without a few pricks that needed to be soothed by Mother's salves from her medicine box.

"The few Indians who populate this area don't have the least sense of the good land for growin' this country is," said Father. "If they would just learn to use the hoe an' some seed, they wouldn't have to scrounge the countryside searchin' for the little game there is."

"George, these people are nomadic and sustain themselves by hunting. It will be hard for them to adapt to our ways. Someday they will be forced into a more civilized manner of living, but it seems a shame. Their wild country will be forever shrinking away in the face of an onslaught of white people moving west."

"Hmmph." Father didn't agree. "It's a waste of good resources to have only a handful of Indians holdin' sway over so much good land."

"But they have, I should say *had,* immense freedom. They roam the land and take from it everything they need. At least they could before their contact with the white man. Why can't we, I mean the white people as a whole, be content with what we have? Why do we have to take their land from them?"

"We ain't takin' their land, Tamsen."

"Are not taking, George. No, not us. But what Americans desire of this kind they always effect and it is useless to oppose. As we travel through their land we use up the grass, foul the water, hunt and kill the animals. We take these things from them. George, can't you understand what I'm saying?"

"I ain't—I'm not hankerin' to have anythin' to do with the Indians or their country. We have to cross their land, an' they're gettin' their price by all their beggin' an' stealin'. Over the ages people have conquered other people an' made 'em change their way of livin' an' all. Just read the bible, it tells of more conquests than I can count."

"But do you think that is what God intended? Not likely! But every time one nation conquers another, they invoke a God-given right."

Father threw his hands up and went off to Uncle Jacob's camp, muttering to himself.

We crossed a stream called Vermillion Creek. It was the largest stream we'd crossed since leaving the Kansas and had very steep banks.

"Notice this here current's much stronger than what we been experiencin'?" said Father to Uncle Jacob. "Bryant tells me that we're climbin' slow like—that after a time we'll be to a much higher elevation in the Rocky Mountains."

That evening as we were making camp on a rise on the prairie, a terrible storm struck. We dashed for the wagon, covering ourselves with blankets. Terrific explosions of electricity split the sky and peal upon peal of thunder rolled up and down the heavens. It was terrifying. Deafening. The rain fell for hours in cold, shivering floods that misted through the wagon canvas, wetting everything.

The following morning came dark and gloomy with a howling wind that pierced us through our soaked clothing to our very bones. We were delayed starting off because one of our drivers was sick. He was put in one of the wagons where he lay moaning all morning.

"He's sick from a drinking spree," said Mother. "Where did he get the spirits?"

"I think several in the company have whiskey to sell to the Indians," said Father.

"They have no business doing that. It is carrying the bane of our civilization to a people that cannot resist it. It is disgusting to me that some of our so-called Christians will sell whiskey to the Indians, not caring what ungodly actions they are then driven to do to obtain more."

We reached bluffs overlooking the Big Blue River. A thunderstorm raged throughout most of the night, scaring us with deafening crashes of thunder, lightning and raging torrents of water. The wet, the cold, and the struggle to keep the tents and gear from blowing away caused much irritation in the company.

"I never encountered so many cantankerous and onery people," said Aunt Betsey to Mother.

"Their hearts have become bad, as the Indians say."

"The committee had another meeting and enacted some more rules, but it won't do no good. I heard that some of the men started fighting. They won't allow the women to have a say, but they'd likely make better work of it."

The Blue was wide, deep and rapid and so much swollen from the rain that we were not able to cross. The women brought out tubs and kettles and began washing the Kansas dirt from clothes and bedding.

"If childbirth don't get'cha, washin' will surely do you in," griped Aunt Betsey. "My arms and hands are swole up and blistered red."

"Betsey, I have a salve you can use on your arms. I told our men that I'd wash their clothes if they would bathe. They smell like pigs. But George told them to wash their own clothes and bathe too. I'm relieved, it's hard just to do ours."

"Our teamster, Jim Smith, he's smarter than the rest. He's sparkin' that daughter of Mr. Brunell an' gettin' her to do his wash. The other boys are looking to do the same. Brunell's wonderin' why his old maid daughter is all a'sudden so popular."

We helped Elitha and Leanna spread the wet clothes over the bushes nearby. I was startled when I saw a strange looking man next to a wagon nearby. He was sitting on a stump, working on a harness.

I went to Mother, tugging on her sleeve.

"Mother, why does that man look so strange?"

Straightening up slowly, she looked to where I was pointing. "Eliza, he's a Negro. His skin is dark because his ancestors came from a far-off country called Africa. Most of the people there have black skin."

"How did he come here?"

"Most likely he was brought here, or he was born here, into slavery. Come, we will talk to him."

We walked to where the man sat. I hung back, a little afraid of the strange man.

"Good afternoon, I am Mrs. George Donner, and this is my daughter, Eliza."

"Pleased, lady. I'm called Angus."

"Eliza is curious about your dark skin, and I have explained to her that you are African. Are you a freedman?"

"No, Missus, I don' wanna be no freedman. Massa Bo-man, he done tol' me 'bout all dat, but I say I born on de home place an' I don know how to be any place but wit my own people. They goin' to the far country, so I goin' too."

"So you know that there is no slavery in the Oregon territory?"

"Yes'm, I know dat, but I ain't goin' to leave my home folks."

A man approached us, taking off a big straw hat and bowing slightly. "Ah'm Jonathan Bowman, from Kentucky. Y'all Miz Donner? Ah've met your husband."

"Yes, and this is Eliza, my daughter. She was curious about Angus, she's never seen a Negro."

"Ma'am, he's been freed to do as he wishes, but understand, it's not an easy thing for a slave that knows no other life."

"Yes. Well! We must be getting back. Good-day, Angus, Mr. Bowman."

I told Father about Mother taking me to meet the black man and meeting Mr. Bowman.

Father looked apprehensive. "Mother, I hope you didn't put forth your New England blue-blood abolitionist view on slavery—"

"No, George, I did not!"

There was another lightning storm during the night and in the morning two oxen were found dead, struck by lightning. As we lay by in camp waiting for the waters to recede we explored the area. We found a beautiful spring of water flowing from a ledge of rocks into a pool ten feet below. Mr. Bryant named the place Alcove Springs.

The water continued very high. A call was made for workers to build rafts. Two large cottonwood trees were felled from which canoes were hollowed out and a cross-frame made to fit the wheels of the wagons. When the craft was finished it was christened "Blue River Rover" and all commenced to cheer as the new ferry floated down the river to the embarkation point.

It was at Alcove Springs that Mrs. Reed's mother, Mrs. Keyes, died. Mother was sad because she could not effect a cure.

"I attended to her as best I could, and I feel that my medicines did relieve her suffering. She'll be buried here, but James promised Margaret that they will return and take her mother back to Illinois."

After the funeral service the men commenced to cross the wagons over the Big Blue. The animals had to be driven across, one man on a horse in front to lead, others behind to urge the beasts forward. There was much snorting and bellowing, and then nothing could be seen except heads floating upon the water, all the way to the other shore.

Soon masses of black clouds rolled in and it began to rain. The men were shaking with fatigue and cold by the time the last wagons were taken across. A fall in temperature made the night extremely uncomfortable, seeming like the middle of winter.

In the morning we moved from the bottom land of the Blue to a high rolling prairie. We came across two graves by the side of the road and gathered some wild flowers to place on the small humps of ground.

Mother knelt down to straighten the markers. "These poor little children, left in this wilderness with no one to care for their graves. How their mothers must suffer!"

We traveled into an area where water from the streams and springs was very bad, causing us to suffer terrible bouts of stomach upsets.

Father was vexed with the troubles and disagreements within the wagon company. "Seems like each day we have more an' more cranky people an' fightin'. Today an argument between McClary and Miller that's been simmerin' boiled over. Miller, the owner of the oxen, wanted to take them from the wagon an' McClary, the owner of the wagon, refused. Things was gettin' so wrought up that a meetin' was called, but before anythin' was decided the men took to fightin' an' hittin' each other. Miller went for a weapon an' was stopped. Another meetin' was held and some of the people headed for Oregon have agreed to separate from the main company and they're takin' the two quarrelin' men with 'em."

"Some people improve upon acquaintance, others don't. It's good not to have trouble," said Mother, "but I'm sad to part with the friends we've made."

In the group that was separating from the company there was a man who owned a small mule named Willy. The mule developed an attachment for our mare, Margaret. When the people bound for Oregon left us, Willy left with his master but soon appeared on our march happily trotting alongside our mare. Willy's owner, Mr. Tibbets, was very unhappy as he had to travel many miles to collect him. His displeasure came to a boil on his second trip to get Willy, and he began

beating him, holding his head tight with a rope around his neck, hitting him hard with a stick. The mule would bray and dance away as each blow descended.

Father came up. "Mister, lay off on that animal. Beating him ain't goin' to work. He's plumb fixiated."

Mr. Tibbets stopped, took a handkerchief out of his pocket and wiped his face with it. "I'm tuckered out, chasin' this stupid mule."

"Mr. Tibbets," said Mother, "we'll buy Willy from you. Our girls can ride him."

Mr. Tibbets was preparing to give Willy another whack but he stopped and squinted at Mother, his lips parting as he sucked on his tobacco stained teeth. "How much you plan on paying?" he asked, a crafty look coming on his face.

He patted Willy affectionately. "This mule is the best natured critter I ever seen, not contrary like most mules." Mr. Tibbets stamped his foot in the soft dirt, sending a puff of dust over Mother's skirt. "I won't take less than thirty dollars!"

"That's robbery. That mule ain't worth five dollars, an' we don't need no mule to be a bother to us," said Father.

"Willy's not a bother at all, George. Give Mr. Tibbets thirty dollars. Just consider it ransom."

Leanna and Frances held Willy's rope while Father lifted Georgia and me onto his back. Leanna started giggling. "He looks like a beaver when he sucks on his teeth."

"Willy sucks on his teeth?"

"No, Frances. Mr. Tibbets does."

It was open country without an end, spreading away now flat and then rolling, going on clear to the sky, as far as we could see. It was unbearably hot.

We usually walked a distance off from the wagon to get away from the dust. Mother would look for vegetables and fruits to include in our meals and plants that she could use as medicines. When she found a plant that was new to her, she would take a flower or leaf and place it in a notebook and sometimes she would draw a picture of the plant. One day, she spied a patch of prickly pear and determined to harvest some. We tried to help, but the sharp needles discouraged us. That evening Mother boiled the clumps until the needles dropped off and then fried the interiors.

"What kind of vittles is this?" asked Aunt Betsey.

"It's the hearts of prickly pear. They're delicious, and good for you," said Mother. "It will help keep us from getting scurvy."

"What's scurvy?" asked Frances.

"It's a condition that is very unpleasant. Terrible sores develop all over the body and in the mouth and gums. In the old days mariners on long voyages would die from it. Then it was discovered that certain foods could effect a recovery. If we cannot find fresh foods along our way our supply of dry fruit will be gone before our journey is over. I brought some crystals of citric acid to use just in case. That's what I use to make our lemonade."

There were numerous accidents and breakdowns of the wagons. One day it was Mr. Bryant's wagon. The wagon train moved on, but several in the group stopped to help. While the men were working on the wagon, the women took advantage of the time to catch up on chores. Mother was baking pies, so we little girls followed cousin Solomon to explore a nearby gully. We were walking along when he suddenly stopped. "Shhh! Don't move! It's a rattler."

Frances and Georgia ran to a safe distance, but I stood transfixed, fascinated by the snake as it coiled tighter and tighter. Solly bent over and picked up a branch, snapping parts of it off to make a fork. Then he started poking at the snake with the branch. Suddenly it struck at Solly, but he knocked it away with the stick and jumped to the side. The snake landed beside me, all stretched out. I screamed but I couldn't move. Then Solly speared the snake's head in the fork of the stick, and we all trooped back to camp.

Solly held his trophy up in the air, the body curling and whipping as it tried to free itself. The terrible mouth gaped open, its tongue flashing and curling between dripping fangs.

"Auntie Tamsen," called Solomon, "look what we found."

Mother dropped the pan she was holding and grabbed Father's rifle, yelling at Solomon to drop the snake and get out of the way. The blast missed the snake, which was making a retreat, passing under one of the wagons and heading toward another. Men began yelling and grabbing their weapons, with Mother screaming and pointing at the departing creature. Shot after shot followed, all missing. Finally, one of the men picked up a big rock and threw it down on the snake's head. It twitched for a few moments and then was still.

We were mesmerized with fright and it took a few moments for us to realize the excitement was over. Mother grabbed a limb off the firewood pile and began switching Solomon with it. "How could you do such a fool thing around my girls?"

Father took the stick from Mother. "Honey, the girls are all right. It was just a prank."

"Yes, but what might have happened!"

Mr. Bryant picked up the dead snake. "If no one else wants it, I'll take it. I've heard they're quite edible."

"Mr. Bryant, I'd like some of the skin to make a hat band before you cut it up," said Solomon.

"All right. Do you like snake meat?"

"I never et none, but I'm willin' to give it a try."

Solly related his experience to the campfire gathering that evening. "It was prickly eatin', with all the little ribs." Then he started laughing. "Mr. Bryant held it over the fire on a stick to cook an' it commenced to curl and coil all over again, scaring the b'jesus out'ta Mr. Bryant. He about jumped out'ta his pants. One of the men said it was the muscles contractin' from the heat."

The next day we came up to another stream that had steep banks, causing a delay as the wagons were eased forward. We sat down under a cottonwood tree on the bank of the stream and watched the wagons skitter one by one down the side of the near bank and then slowly ascend the other side, pulled by the oxen in front and pushed by sweating and cursing men in back.

As we watched, one of the wagons began to tilt. Several people shouted a warning, but once started, the wagon could not be stopped from falling. The helping men jumped out of the way as the wagon fell over on its side, throwing a woman and small child and most of the contents of the wagon into the water. Our wagons passed while the capsized wagon was pulled out of the stream. Mother helped pick up the things that had spilled out and then we moved on.

"No one was hurt, but they'll have to lay by because the pole of the wagon broke," said Father. "The man's got help. He's travelin' with other Dutchmen."

Aunt Betsey and Mother discussed the German family while finishing up the chores that evening.

"I feel sorry for her," said Aunt Betsey. "Her husband treats her terrible like. Miz Hoppe said she's seen him beatin' on her. And her so far along with child. Somethin' should be done about it."

"Done about what?" asked Father, who was sitting nearby talking to Mr. Reed.

"You know the man that had the turned-over wagon today?"

"Name's Keseberg."

"We cannot abide the way he treats his wife," said Mother. "He has a violent temper. He takes out his anger on her and beats her."

"I've heard he's downright unsociable."

"I wish that you would speak to him."

"We ain't gonna interfere in another man's affairs."

"If you saw this man approach another with the intent to batter him or shoot or knife him, what would you do?" asked Mother.

"That's not the same thing."

Mother sounded irritated. "George, don't resort to just being stubborn! It's an assault no matter how you look at it."

"We ain't gettin' involved in somethin' that's none of our affair."

"No, George," said Mr. Reed. "A man who is brutal to women disgusts me. I will tell him he will be removed from the company if he does not desist."

Later, Mother talked to Father about Mr. Reed. "James is a difficult man to understand, George. Perhaps his sympathy is genuine, but I wonder if he's concerned about Mrs. Keseberg from real feelings of sympathy or from a compulsion to exert his will over others."

"It ain't ... "

"George, you made your point. And please stop saying ain't!"

Day after day, week after week, the company went through the same weary routine. Getting up before day-break, cooking food over a fire of scrub-oak, buffalo chips, or sagebrush. Then packing up the coffee pot and camp kettle, rushing to put everything away and gather up the children before the wagons rolled, only to do everything in reverse that evening.

As we journeyed along we would find buffalo skulls, pieces of board, or paper stuck onto a stick with messages and notices written on them. Sometimes it would be lost livestock, sometimes notice of problems with Indians, or people leaving word for family or friends following on the trail. We little ones had chores and one chore was to gather buffalo chips. At one point in the journey there were no trees, and buffalo chips were used as fuel for our fires. At first we complained about how "yucky" it was but after a while we got used to it. The trick to it was not to pick it up until you had kicked it over because there were crawly things that lived underneath.

The bleached white bones of the buffalo littered the plains, but still the live creatures were not seen. Every dark object spotted upon the horizon caused a chase, only to be something else. Numerous antelope were seen, but they were too fast for our hunters. One evening we had just pitched camp when a man approached, leading a horse with a dead antelope draped over it.

"Your horse must be a fast one to bag an antelope," Father said to him. The man held up a long stick with a handkerchief tied to it. "I didn't use my horse. I used this here stick. The antelope is a curious critter and when he sees you moving this handkerchief back an' forth, real slow like, he wants to know what it is."

"How long did you lay out?"

"I went ahead this mornin'. I seen tracks where they go to water an' I went off an' waited. Toward evenin' they came along an' I jes' kept on movin' the stick an' this here buck he couldn't resist seein' if there was somethin' he should know about an' I got him."

We reached the Platte River. It was quite shallow with a sluggish flow, and tasted terrible. Mother told us the river marked a milestone for our journey and that we would follow it for hundreds of miles

As the sun rose high in the heavens so did the swarms of gigantic and ferocious mosquitoes. They lit upon us in such numbers we found ourselves in frenzies of flailing and whipping and jumping about.

Sometimes Mother held school when the train was stopped but mostly we just ran and played and had a great time.

Our trail was continually crossed by deep paths made by the buffalo, but it wasn't until mid-June that a buffalo was killed and it was reported that a large number of the creatures had been spotted. This caused a stir among the men and they began cleaning their rifles and sharpening their knives.

This activity very nearly caused a serious accident in our camp. Solomon had gone out hunting without shooting anything. When he returned to camp he placed his charged weapon in the wagon amongst some bedding, planning to go out again after our noon stop. As we were eating we heard a rifle bellow very close by but we didn't think much of it until Uncle Jacob came running.

"Where's Solomon?" he shouted at Betsey. "That stupid boy a' yourn left a charged gun in the wagon. It's lucky I wasn't kilt! I'm gonna whup him good!"

Solomon was sitting on a wagon tongue eating and looked up in alarm when he heard Uncle Jacob yelling his name. Uncle grabbed Solomon by the arm and pushed him outside of the wagons.

"Pa! I'm sorry. I'm sorry."

"A man was killed just recent this same fool way! He had no more sense than you!"

Betsey followed them. "Jacob, it was an accident. Don't hit him."

She pulled on Jacob's arm, causing him to lose his balance, fall-down. Solomon ran off. Uncle tried to get up, but couldn't.

"Noah, give me a hand," said Father, "let's get him over to the shade."

"I just lost my breath, that's all," wheezed Uncle.

"You got no call to hit him, it was an accident," said Aunt Betsey.

"You goin' up agin' your husband?" Uncle gasped, glaring at Betsey. "I'm a'gonna beat the tar out'a him. Let me be, I jes' need to rest fer a minute."

"I have medicine," said Mother. "If we can get him to take it, it might relieve his distress."

Father took the medicine to Uncle every day until he got better. After a week Aunt Betsey found Solomon staying with a family in one of the forward companies and brought him back.

We were stopped for our noon break a few days later when Mr. Keseberg came to our camp looking very worried. He came to Mother with hat in hand.

"Please excuse this interruption in your meal, Mrs. Donner. I beg of you to come to my wife. It is her time and she needs a woman's help."

"Yes. Let me gather up some things."

Mother took her medicine bag and some other articles from the wagon. "Elitha, you mind the little ones. I am going with Mr. Keseberg to see after his wife."

It was after dark and we were already in our beds when Mother returned. "Mother, I was just about to come and get you," exclaimed Father. "You don't need this extra worry, especially with them people."

We peeked out where the canvas cover didn't quite meet the side-board of the wagon.

"I wasn't alone, Mrs. Dunbar came to help. Mrs. Keseberg had a difficult time, a breech birth. She's very weak, but I'm sure both will be fine. My God, but it was *hot* in that wagon. Mr. Keseberg refused to stop and we were jostled and banged around with no decent place to sit, the flies driving us crazy. Oh, no! He had to go full chisel. That man is an ass!"

We gasped. We'd heard Father say things like that, but not *Mother*.

May 27, 1846

This evening we camped on a high elevation of the prairie. As we were making camp a violent storm struck with thunder, lightning & a torrential downpour. It is almost worth the violent attack as the air is cleansed & we are free of the choking dust. A meeting was held yesterday morning to draw up more regulations for the governance of the wagon train. In these assemblies some of the men become very combative & the use of violent language is common. A motion was made to appoint a committee to try the officers when charged with tyranny or neglect of duty & was carried, whereupon all the officers resigned. Mr. Bryant was dismayed at the course of events & asked the company to reconsider the vote. The company then voted to the opposite effect and reelected the officers. This is the dilemma of emigrant life where no law prevails except the will of the people. Unfortunately, there are men and women in the emigrating parties who endeavor to produce discord which causes much dissension, waste of time and innumerable meetings.

Chapter Three

We were now on the open plains
and in the country of the Pawnee Indians

June 16, 1846
My Old friend:
We are now on the Platte, 200 miles from Fort Laramie. Our journey, so far, has been pleasant. The roads have been good, & food plentiful.

The water for a part of the way has been indifferent—but at no time have our cattle suffered for it. Wood is now very scarce, but buffalo chips are excellent—they kindle quickly and retain heat surprisingly. We had this evening buffalo steaks broiled upon them that had the same flavor they would have had upon hickory coals.

We feel no fear of Indians. Our cattle graze quietly around our encampment unmolested. Two or three men will go hunting twenty miles from camp & last night two of our men lay out in the wilderness rather than ride their horses after a hard chase. Indeed if I do not experience something far worse than I have yet done, I shall say the trouble is all in getting started.

Our wagons have not needed much repair, but I cannot yet tell in what respects they may be improved. Certain it is they cannot be too strong. Our preparations for the journey, in some respects, might have been bettered. Bread has been the principal article of food in our camp. We laid in 150 lbs. of flour & 75 lbs. of meat for each individual & I fear bread will be scarce. Meat is abundant. Rice and beans are good articles on the road—cornmeal, too, is very acceptable. Linsey dresses are the most suitable for children. Indeed, if I had one it would be comfortable.

We are now 450 miles from Independence. Our route at first was rough and through a timbered country that appeared to be fertile. After striking the prairie we found a first-rate road & the only difficulty we have had has been crossing creeks. In that, however, there has been no danger. I never could have believed we could have traveled so far with so little difficulty. The prairie between the Blue and Platte rivers is beautiful beyond description. Never have I seen so varied a country—so suitable for cultivation. Everything was new and pleasing. The Indians frequently come to see us, & the chiefs of a tribe breakfasted at our tent this morning. All are so friendly that I cannot help feeling sympathy & friendship for them. But on one sheet, what can I say?

Since we have been on the Platte we have had the river on one side & the ever varying mounds on the other—and have traveled through the bottom lands from one to ten miles wide with little or no timber. The soil is sandy, & last year, on account of the dry season, the emigrants found grass here scarce. Our cattle are in good order & where proper care has been taken, none has been lost. Our milk cows have been of great service—indeed, they have been of more advantage than our meat. We have plenty of butter and milk. We are commanded by Capt. Russell—an amiable man. George Donner is himself yet. He crows in the morning, & shouts out "Chain up, boys! Chain up!" with as much authority as though he was "something in particular". John Denton is still with us—we find him a useful man in camp. Hiram Miller and Noah James are in good health & doing well. We have of the best of people in our company, & some, too, that are not so good.

Buffalo show themselves frequently. We have found the wild tulip, the

primrose, the lupine, the ear-drop, the larkspur and creeping hollyhock,
& a beautiful flower resembling the bloom of the beech tree, but in
bunches large as a small sugar-loaf & of every variety of shade, to red
and green. I botanize & read some, but cook a "heap" more.

There are 420 wagons, as far as we have heard, on the road between
here and Oregon and California. Give our love to all inquiring friends,
God bless them,
Mrs. George Donner

We plodded on through a vast expanse of flat earth—treeless plains unbroken by bush or rock. The sun glared down upon us with a pitiless heat, the distant blue prairie quivering under it. Here and there a crow, raven or buzzard circled languidly overhead.

The wind blew gritty dust into us, kicked up by the wheels of the train. It entered our mouths, noses, and eyes, choking us so that it was hard to breathe. It got between our teeth, a constant grit that couldn't be washed out because the water was full of the dirt too.

Mother said that it was the alkali in the dust that caused our eyes to burn and hurt. She washed our eyes with one of her medicines and doctored the eyes of our oxen with it too. Some oxen in the train were affected so badly by the dust that they became blinded.

One evening after supper there was more excitement in the talk than usual.

"Russell's resigned his post," reported Father. "The rest of us will resign too. I'm happy to give it up. I'm tired of all the vexations."

"I heard Bryant's leavin' the group," said Uncle.

"Yes," replied Father. "He doesn't like the progress of the company. He an' about nine others are plannin' to buy mules at Fort Laramie an' continue on packin'. Russell's going with 'em." Father got up and started kicking dirt over the last embers of the fire. "If we're at

Independence Rock by the fourth of July, we're doin' fine. I think we'll make it. I'm turnin' in. I'm some tired from fightin' the wind an' the dust all day. This is the gol-durndest country for wind."

We were now on the south fork of the Platte River, near where the trail diverged from the stream and crossed over it to the north fork. There were large herds of buffalo all around, some of which approached so close that there was danger of their mingling with our loose herds of cattle. In places they were crowded so densely together that in the distance their rounded backs presented a surface of uniform blackness. Amid the multitude rose little columns of dust where some of them were rolling on the ground. Here and there bulls would be battling, and we could hear the clattering of their horns and their hoarse bellowing.

"I'll be glad when we have some distance from them," said Father, "they're dangerous. If they're alarmed, they'll raise up an' the whole herd will start a stampede. It wouldn't be good to be in their way."

"The Indians are very skilled at killing the buffalo while on the run," said Mr. Reed. "They have horses that they train especially for the hunt. But I assure you, none are as good as my horse, Glaucus."

"That so?" asked Uncle Jacob.

"That is so. Tomorrow I will prove to this doubting company that my horse and I are as good at hunting buffalo as any of the so-called professionals."

The next day a buffalo hunt was organized. Mr. Reed and two of our teamsters participated in the hunt. When they returned with several of the choicer parts of a buffalo, Mr. Reed felt compelled to brag.

"I was very successful. My purpose was that the hunters might see that a *sucker* had the best horse in the company and was the best and most daring horseman in the caravan."

Mother and Father were talking about this later and Frances asked Mother what the word "sucker" meant.

"Well, it wasn't nice of whoever used that term to Mr. Reed, but I think they meant that he might be considered a "greenhorn", someone who is new at doing something."

A day later Mother became very upset when Mr. Reed ran a wounded buffalo into the camp. The beast was crazy with fear, snorting and dashing here and there, spilling and breaking camp gear as it ran and jumped through the wagons with Mr. Reed trailing it on his horse, trying to turn it away.

"That was a stupid thing for him to do and I told him so," Mother told Father. "He very nearly caused injury to Mrs. Dunlap and her children."

"Tamsen, most men don't take kindly to bein' chastised as if you were their school marm."

"Well, he needed chastising. Mrs. Dunlap is prostrate in her tent, hysterical from the experience."

"Well, she needs to get up and get on with her work. Nobody was hurt," said Father.

The company suffered from more and more disagreements and annoyance. Two quarrelsome men in the company engaged in an argument that resulted in the shooting of one.

"They called it an accident," said Father. "I don't reckon it was, but the committee let it go. Seems like when mankind gets away from the restraints of society an' law their animal natures start showin' through. Bryant did what he could for the man, he doesn't think he'll live."

We crossed the ridge between the South and North Platte rivers, a distance of some twenty miles. It was through some of the roughest country we had seen, all ridges, mounds, deep hollows, and sand, with sparse vegetation and the only water a stagnant pond or two.

The road struck directly up a bluff, rising quite rapidly at first, then very gradually for about twelve miles when we reached the summit and a most magnificent view. Before and below us the river wound its way through broken hills and green meadows.

Behind us was the prairie over which we had just passed. On our right, the gradual convergence of the two valleys, and immediately at our feet Ash Creek, which fell off suddenly into deep chasms. The entry into the hollow was particularly difficult. Ahead of us a wagon overturned and two oxen were killed and several injured.

The men double-rough-locked the wagons, removing all but one yoke of oxen and began the descent. After reaching the hollow we found a pure cold spring and patches of currants and gooseberries. In this place there was an old cabin that served the purpose of a post office. Inside was a niche where people had placed letters waiting for anyone passing east to carry them on to the settlements.

The next morning we learned of a tragic occurrence in a company ahead of us on the road. A man started out in the middle of the night to take his turn at guard duty and feeling the night cold, he wrapped his blanket around his shoulders for warmth. His son thought the approaching figure was an Indian, took aim, and fired. They buried the man in the road, scattering the ashes of the campfire over his grave, hoping that the Indians would not find it.

For several miles the trail passed over sandy soil and the wheels

sank deeply. This valley of the Platte River was very rough, hilly and parched looking. We came upon a spire which was called Chimney Rock, then bluffs which resembled buildings with wings and domes, and a craggy flat-topped mountain known as Scott's Bluff.

"The name derives from a man named Scott," said Mother. "He was in company with a group of trappers when he became ill and was left in the boat to die as his companions traveled on. One wonders about the frailties of man to leave a companion to die all alone in this barren wilderness."

The trail left the river as we approached Scott's Bluff, crossing a level plain and ascending a ridge. As we reached the summit of the ridge, we had our first glimpse of the Rocky Mountains. Father thought the peak we saw way off was Laramie Peak and then in the far, far distance, the Wind River Mountains.

The day was pleasant and we walked with Mother off to the side of the wagons to remove ourselves from the tortured shriek of the wheels and the dust.

"This country has such a magnificence," said Mother. "It's raw and untamed, but it's good to have open space, a freedom—"

"I think it's ugly," exclaimed Elitha. "No trees, no green grass. All broken up and jagged. Will California be like this? If it is I'll hate it."

"We've been told that where we are going, to the northern part, there are gentle rolling hills covered with oak trees," said Mother. "We can expect that in the winter, the land will be green, but in the summer there is hardly any rain, and everything dries up and turns a golden color. The summers are rather hot, but the air is dry. The heat is not as bothersome as what we had in Illinois."

"And there's an ocean," said Georgia.

"Oh yes, a big ocean. I grew up near the Atlantic Ocean, and I miss it. I have heard that the Pacific is much nicer, more gentle, and warmer. We will not have opportunity to visit the ocean any time soon, because it will take a while to get settled and we won't have time to sight-see.

Look, I think the wagons are stopping to make camp. We'd better get back."

A few miles east of Fort Laramie we came across a small building of logs, which was a trading post of sorts, and we felt that we were again touched by civilization. There was a congregation of old traders and trappers there and this is where we first encountered the Sioux tribe of Indians. They had recently returned from a war against the Pawnees with twenty-five scalps and many captured horses.

As our wagons approached the trading post, a throng of Indian horsemen appeared and circled our wagons at a full gallop, each warrior's long hair, adorned with eagle's feathers, flying behind him in the wind. A chief, in splendid attire, rode before them, mounted on a black and white horse.

After circling two or three times, the cavalcade moved off, singing war songs, which sounded similar to the yipping of coyotes. That evening our wagon group hosted a dinner for the traders and others of the fort. Mother asked one of the traders if he could speak the Sioux language.

"Yes'm, but just enough to get my tradin' done. Now, New, he talks it good."

"Which man is Mr. New?"

He pointed to a man sitting cross-legged on the ground, a small pipe in one hand and a cup of coffee in the other. He wore buckskins and moccasins, and his pepper-gray hair was tied back in a horse's tail. He arose from the ground as we approached, his faded blue eyes squinting out from under brows as thick as a bird's nest.

"Mr. New?"

"Yes, ma'am. I'm New."

"I'm Mrs. George Donner. My husband and I are members of the wagon company."

"Right pleased to meet'cha, ma'am."

"You speak the Sioux language?"

"Yes ma'am. I been with an' around the Injuns fer twenty years or more."

"I would like to visit one of their doctors or healers."

"No, ma'am. That wouldn't be likely. They don't have doctors like you're a'thinkin'. Their doctors are called shamans. The shamans, they do what you might call hocus pocus. They shake rattles, spit stuff out'a their mouths, sing an' dance around an' such like."

"Do they effect cures?"

"Sometimes the patient gets well, dependin' on if the shaman knows his potions an' cures. These here Injuns know a passel 'bout what plants an' such can cure certain things."

"I've an interest in botany and plant cures. I would like to know what plants they use in healing."

Mr. New knocked the ashes from his pipe. "No, it ain't likely they'd allow it, you bein' a woman, an' a white woman to boot. The shamans, they're real touchy. You see, they depend on fear an' mystery to keep their power, their medicine. They have to convince the Injun that comes to 'em fer a cure that they have the medicine to drive off the bad spirits that's caused the sickness. That's why they do all their hocus pocus, to make the patient believe the shaman has somethin' special that will make a cure.

"It be a tough job. Sometimes if the patient isn't cured, the family will kill the shaman or he loses his standin' an' he don't have a practice no more. Now, in any Injun camp there's gonna be a woman or a man that knows how to use herbs an' plants fer healing."

"Would one of them speak with me?"

"Ma'am, I wouldn't know who those people would be. There's hundreds of Injuns here. I ain't lived in a Injun camp fer many years."

"Perhaps you know of some of their cures?"

Mr. New took out his tobacco pouch and refilled his pipe, tamping down the tobacco. Frances took a small stick out of the fire and held it for him while he puffed on the pipe to get it started. We waited for him to collect his thoughts.

"Now, a partner of mine, a long time back, had a broken leg. We was stayin' with the Sioux fer the winter. We sent fer the head shaman an' he came, but he said it warn't his line of work, and he sent in this Injun who said he was a Bear Dreamer. It seems the Bear Dreamers specialize in broken bones an' such. He looked at the break, an' it was a bad one, the bone comin' through the skin. He said he could fix it, but we'd have to give 'em a horse in payment before he'd start the work. 'Course we were in no position to dicker. After some prelim'aries an' hoopla the Injun mixed up a salve an' smeared it on my friend's leg."

"What was the salve made of?"

Mr. New looked down into his coffee cup and reflected for a moment. "It was bear grease an' som'thin' he called *hu-hwe-han-han pe-zu-la*. This here salve kind'a relaxed my partner, an' then the healer pulled the bone in place an' laced a rawhide 'round the break."

"Your partner didn't have much pain?"

"No, but he'd drunk a pint'a whiskey 'fore the healer got there."

"Was the break cured?"

"He was up an' walkin' around in a couple a'weeks, but had to use a stick to walk with fer a while. He got hisself drowned not too long after that. I'll allow that if we'd been in the white man's camp when he broke his leg, they'd a cut it off an' he'd a been a cripple or died from the gangrene."

Mr. New puffed on his pipe for a moment, then took it from his mouth. "Now, if'n you had gut pains, you'd drink a tea made from horsemint. Fer the trots some take a concoction with lambsquarters, an' fer stomach pain a tea of verbena's good."

He pointed his pipe for emphasis as he thought of something else. "Some claim the root of calamus can help a toothache, but it never helped me none."

"I'm familiar with the plants and cures that you've mentioned, except the calamus. Do you know what it looks like?"

"You use the root. The leaves are kind'a narrow like, yellowish an' green, has a pod that comes out at a angle. It has a spicy smell."

Mother gave Mr. New a page from her notebook and a pencil, and asked him if he would draw the plant.

"I ain't much hand at this, but I'll give it a try."

"That's very good, Mr. New. I know it as sweetflag. The other one, *hu hwe*—"

"Missus, I'll ask around an' see if I can find out an' I'll come to you."

"Are you sure I can't arrange a visit?"

"Yes'm, it don't pay to get close to the Injuns. They might hold you fer ransom. The Sioux're not wrathy right now, but you never know."

After dinner we all went to watch a shooting demonstration. The Indians showed much skill and proficiency with the bow and arrow, attaining great distance with accuracy. We didn't stay long, as it was hot and we little ones begged to go back. That evening at the campfire, the people were all abuzz talking about an accident that happened after we left. A mountaineer's rifle had burst as he fired at a target.

"See, this is how it happened," related one of the men. "Old Bill was wantin' a new rifle. He looks at ever' rifle in the camp 'til he found one he considered the best of the bunch. Someone tried to talk him out'a the purchase, tellin' him it was a unlucky gun an' that with it the owner had accidentally shot an' prit' near killed a man, an' had clipped a piece off the ear of another. Bill didn't cotton to this suggestion that he did'n know a good gun when he saw one. He allowed he'd hunted an' trapped in the mountains fer sixty years an' nobody could teach him anythin' about a rifle.

"He tells the greenhorn, 'Just get back under your wagon an' mend your moccasins.' So he pays fer the rifle an' marked off a hundred 'n fifty yards an' put up a target. He loaded the gun heavy to see how she would carry fer the distance."

The story teller raised his arm in demonstration, pulling an imaginary trigger. "He aimed at the mark an' fired. Blowie! The rifle burst the breech, a piece 'a the barrel split out, the stock blew to pieces, an' the lock flew fifty feet away. The blast knocked Ol' Williams flat on his back, full a' splinters. They thought he was dead an' was discussin' what to do with him when someone poured some whiskey down his throat an' he comes to. Then, he gets up an' staggers into the post proclaimin' that nothin' could kill him, much less a blamed rifle."

A report came to us that the Pawnee Indians had ran off a hundred head of stock in a company about ten days ahead of us. Two men were killed when they attempted to recover the stock. Another company about three miles ahead of us had a party of twenty or thirty Pawnees attempt to break into their camp, but they managed to keep them off. These events caused quite a bit of alarm in the companies and several families turned back.

Three men from another train came to Mr. Bryant, begging him to assist a boy whose leg had been crushed under the wheels of a wagon. Mr. Bryant returned the next day and told us what had happened.

"The child's leg was already in a gangrenous state and he was near death. The injury occurred days ago and had been wrapped up, but that was the extent of the treatment. I felt there was no point in causing more pain by an amputation, but the mother insisted and a man stepped forward saying he would take off the leg. The poor little fellow died before the procedure was completed."

Mr. Bryant made a gesture of helplessness and rose tiredly from his seat by our campfire. "It's been a long day, I'll say good-night."

"I should get out my journal," said Mother, sighing. "Look, girls, the dust has settled. I can see the stars."

"What makes stars?" asked Georgia.

"Well, I cannot say, but in the Bible it says that God put lights in the expanse of the sky to separate the day from the night, to serve as signs to mark seasons and days and years, and give light on earth."

We gazed upward for awhile, enthralled.

"It's so beautiful, I could stay here all night to watch the stars move. One day I shall tell you more but now it is time for bed."

Mother knew about so many things. She seemed so different from the other women. I thought about this many times in later years, trying to recall everything I could of my mother, missing her so much that the ache inside filled my whole being.

The next evening we accompanied Mother to take Mrs. Keyes, Mrs. Reed's mother, some medicine.

"The journey is so hard on her, Tamsen," said Mrs. Reed. "I know this terrible dust is causing more distress."

"I have given her some laudanum, which should help her sleep, and I put some medicine in her eyes. I hope that it will relieve the pain."

"Oh, how I hated to subject her to this journey!" cried Mrs. Reed.

"Why was James so adamant that you must go this year? You could have waited, surely your Mother could not have survived to next spring. You should have put your foot down and refused."

"A woman does what her husband requests, Tamsen. I suppose some women of the lower class might deny a husband his right—"

"Right? Please, Margaret, spare me."

"Tamsen, you were reluctant to make the journey. Are you telling me that I should have refused my husband's wish when you— "

Mother made a gesture of impatience. "If I had a sick mother, there would be nothing that could take me away, and that includes a husband with a tickle-foot looking for green grass on the other side of the fence. I *agreed* to go, I was not ordered."

"James had his reasons. It was a decision forced upon us and not entirely—"

"Yes. These are hard times to be in business." Mother stood up from her seat by the wagon and took my hand. "Come, babe, we must go back. Margaret, I'll come tomorrow with more medicine."

We began the walk back to our camp. Mother held the lantern up so we could see to walk back to our wagons. A voice boomed into the night.

"Who is this enjoying the night air? Ahh, it is Mrs. Donner, the little medicine woman."

"Good evening, Mr. Russell. Are you feeling any better?"

"A small improvement and I thank you for your ministrations. I followed your instructions implicitly! What was that you said? This is to amuse the patient while nature cures the disease? You are most profound, dear lady! Now, if you have somethin' in your medicine bag to sprinkle in the food to make this company more agreeable, I would be grateful."

"Mr. Russell, the task is hopeless."

"I believe you're right."

He slapped at his face. "Damnation! The mosquitoes are worse here than any place ah've ever been. The whole night is filled with the whinin' of their wings!"

Mr. Russell moved away into the dark. "I must check on the night guards. Last night several of the stock got away which necessitated a delay while we rounded them up this mornin'. Seems ever' day there's somethin' that keeps us from leavin' promptly. Thanks to a good and gracious God, my duties with this company will be ended tomorrow at Fort Laramie."

Chapter Four

*At Fort Laramie all eyes turned
to a great spectacle spread out over the plain.*

The fort was situated on the Laramie River near its junction with the Platte, surrounded by a plain. We gazed in awe at the hundreds of conical shaped tents spread out across the valley, resembling fields of hay gathered into stacks.

The plain was alive with activity and galloping Indian horsemen, showing off their prowess and their exotic costumes. A steady stream of people walked to and from a large mud-walled stockade.

At the fort supplies were purchased and repairs were made to our wagons. Father had brought goods along for the purpose of trade and he bargained with the Indians for buffalo skins and moccasins.

"These Sioux are fixin' to go to war with the Snake an' Crow Indians," said Father. "All that noise they're makin' is their war-dances. They're workin' themselves into frenzy to be in a fightin' mood."

"I think they are being helped along in their endeavors by the effects of whiskey," said Mother.

Mr. New found us at Fort Laramie. "Howdy, ma'am, Mr. Donner." He wiped perspiration off his face with a handkerchief. "Hot, ain't it?

Miz Donner, I found a' Injun woman that knows a lot about cures an' such an' she'll let you talk to her. That is, if you're still of a mind."

"Oh, Mr. New, that's wonderful."

Father didn't like the idea. "Tamsen, are you intendin' goin' into that Indian camp? What are you thinkin'? That's no place for a cultured white lady, nor any white lady."

"George, I want to find out what I can of their use of plants to cure illness. I want to go and Mr. New has already made the arrangements."

"You'd best bring along somethin' to give the woman as a present," said Mr. New. "Miz Donner, the Injuns think it's rude to look at another directly in the eyes. So you need to remember that when we gits with the Injun woman. Where we're goin' is a camp that's led by a chief called White Shield. He's the one that parades around on that big black an' white horse."

Mr. New, Mother, Father, and Mr. Stanton walked to the Indian camp. We watched them make their way across the plain, pausing as several warriors dashed by on their ponies, and again as Indian boys drove a herd of horses down to the river. We saw them approach the edge of the Indian village, disappearing into the dust and smoke haze that hovered over the encampment.

After an hour or so of eager watching, we saw them coming back and ran to meet them. Mother greeted us with a hug. "Children, I am glad to see you, but you must never leave our camp without an adult with you. Never. Do you understand me?"

When we returned to camp Mother made supper and we sat in a circle as we ate our food. Mr. New took his plate and sat down, but before he began eating he cut off a small piece of meat and held it up to the sky four times, then buried it in the soft ground under his feet. He saw us looking at him and grinned sheepishly.

"Learned that from the Injuns. That'll guarantee there'll always be meat. I've had some hungry times."

"We do the same thing, in our way," said Mother.

We were eager for Mother to tell us about her visit to the Indian camp. We waited patiently for supper to be over and finally Mother began.

"Well, it was quite an experience. When we first arrived I was intrigued with a cooking method I observed. They suspend a bag made of an animal hide from a tripod affair of poles. Then they place the food to be cooked in the bag and add very hot stones from a fire. The hot stones bring the food to enough heat to cook the meat or whatever. Oh, but my Lord, the flies! The whole place was quite filthy."

"You gits used to it, ma'am, livin' with 'em," said Mr. New.

"Yes, I guess it's possible," said Mother.

"There was no reason for you to be subjected to that, Mother," said Father. "An' why on earth go back to help an Indian child? What if he screams or somethin' when you doctor him an' they think you're hurting him? They could kill you."

"The Injuns are notional," said Mr. New. "They can be friendly one minute an' jump up an' cleave you with a battle axe the next."

We looked at Mother in alarm, but she was very calm. "I will explain everything to the woman. I think she'll understand."

Mr. New shook his head. "No, most likely there'll be no problem. The woman knows about how medicines work. These Injuns are all het up to make war against other Injuns. The hot-bloods are too wore-out to pay attention to the whites, 'cept to get their whiskey and trade a little."

"Mother, is the boy my age?" asked Frances.

"No, he is older than you. I believe he must be about nine or ten years of age. His eyes are completely shut from the infection." She looked at Father with that expression we knew so well as her "school marm" look. "Going there has caused me no harm, George. I have learned of several medicines and I believe I can help the boy."

"I noticed that there was one lodge house that was bigger than the others," said Mr. Stanton. "It looked like it was more important too. It was painted all over with colored horses. There were men sitting around in front, and it looked to me like it was the Indian version of the country store."

"I was so fixiated on all those vicious dogs that I didn't look around much," said Father.

Mr. Stanton showed us some moccasins and a bag-like container that he had acquired in the Indian camp. "Look at the designs on this parfleche. I am very impressed with the art of these people, especially the beadwork." The bag was made of stiff leather and was decorated very prettily.

"Parfleche is a French-language word," said Mother. "I believe that it has been picked up from French-Canadian fur trappers, meaning the leather that is used to make the bag." She pointed to the decorations. "This is called quill-work. They use the needles from the porcupine. After coloring them with a dye, they flatten them with their teeth or some such mechanism, and sew the quill onto the design." She pointed to another section of the decoration. "They sew beads onto the design too. This work is exquisite."

"They have specialists in their crafts," said Mr. New. "They're paid for the work an' those who do the best beadin' or lodge makin' or such have a good business. Mostly it's done by the women. The men, they specialize in the articles of war an' special powers, what they call their medicine. Miz Donner, just one o' those ribbons you gave the Injun woman would've made her happy. You'll be spoilin' her for the next time a white wants somethin'."

Mother folded a blanket and placed it on a box next to the fire and sat down. "I didn't mind, she obviously was taken with my gift."

She unwrapped a leather packet. "These are the cures that Blue Whirlwind gave me. This one is a root that is used to help with setting broken bones. Remember? Mr. New told us that it was used on his friend. She told us that you smash it up and mix it with bear grease. I don't have bear grease, but I assume any kind of clean grease would have the same effect. She gave me a cure for asthma too."

"The Indians are ignorant savages. It probably don't amount to a hill of beans," Father grumped.

"No, you're wrong there, Mr. Donner," said Mr. New. "The Injuns have a powerful lot of know-how when it comes to remedies. Lot better'n the white doctors that just as soon bleed you to death or wipe you out with purges. Now, I don't mean no offense, just tellin' it true."

He stood up and knocked his pipe against a rock at the fire to empty the tobacco ashes. "I best be getting' on back. I'm spreading my blankets inside the fort. They'll be closin' up the gate."

"Mr. New," asked Father, "have you knowledge of the country south of Fort Bridger? Is there a road whereby one can go south from there to the Salt Lake?"

"No sir, there ain't no road. It be powerful rough country. Nothin' but Injun trails. The only way I know fer wagon parties is to go north by Fort Hall. There's been wagons go that way these last few years. You people thinkin' of takin' that there route that Frémont was on?"

"We're leanin' that way."

"Well, Jim Clyman just came through there with that Hastings feller. He's here now headin' east after bein' on the Pacific Coast. If I was you, I'd find him an' ask him of the route. He knows more about headin' west than just about any man. He was with Jed Smith when they found the South Pass."

The next day Father sought out Mr. Clyman and brought him to join us for our evening meal. "James," said Father, "Clyman here, he tells me he knows you from the Blackhawk War."

Mr. Reed waved a mosquito away from his face, squinting at Mr. Clyman. "Yes, I remember. When did you muster out?"

Mr. Clyman's voice was raspy and he cleared his throat several times before speaking. "I was with Early's comp'ny at Dixon's Ferry, where you were, then with Dodge's Battalion. I mustered out in 1834."

Mr. Clyman was a tall man with bearing and dignity. His light brown hair and clear blue eyes contrasted with a face that was brown and weathered. He had a little twist to his mouth as if he had lost some teeth on one side. Mother dished up a plate of food and he sat down on the ground, cross-legged, to eat.

"Y'all from Illinois? What part?" he asked between mouthfuls.

"Sangamon."

"That right? I spent time there doin' surveyin' work for Colonel Hamilton, think it was in 1821, mebbe '22."

"You've just come from California?"

"That's a fact."

"What do you make of it?"

"Well, some're goin' to like it an' some not. Personally, I think it's a little short of paradise. It depends on what you're lookin' for. Their ranchos are huge, from six to twelve square miles. I passed one which belonged to a Mexican gent that was thirty-three leagues."

"What would that be in acres?"

Mr. Clyman shut his eyes and concentrated. "That's close to one hundred forty thousand acres."

"The hell you say."

"On one I seen only four or five hundred acres was cultivated, the rest was used for grazin'. They had twelve or fifteen thousand head of cattle an' seven or eight thousand head of horses. They don't feed their animals grain. You cain't find a single kernel to feed yer horse in California, but I seen the biggest field of wild oats on the globe, some two or three hundred thousand acres. It falls on the ground to seed the next crop." He hawked and spit, then wiped his mouth on his sleeve.

"What be the situation now with the Mexican government?" someone asked him.

"Well, Frémont caused some alarm by raisin' the American flag at his camp near the Mission of St. John. Then the Mexican general, Castro, raised four hundred men under arms at Monterey. Frémont's bent on conquest an' likely the territory will fly the American flag."

"You came over the California mountains?"

"I did."

"There's a feller, Hastings. He says he knows of a route that's shorter than goin' by Fort Hall. Do you know anythin' of that route?"

Mr. Clyman knocked out ashes from his pipe and refilled it. "Yes, I came through there. I was *with* Hastings."

Getting up, he took a stick from the fire and held it to the tobacco, sucking on the pipe until it was going. He filled his lungs and slowly breathed out the smoke. "He's stayin' up by Fort Bridger waitin' on the emigrants so's he can direct them over this here route. We came through on horses. No wagons've ever gone there an' it will be difficult to do so. The country's full of canyons an' choked with brush."

"Mr. Clyman," said Father, "we'd be obliged if you'd tell us what you can about the country after Bridger's tradin' post."

Mr. Clyman picked up a stick, hunkered down and began drawing some lines in the dirt. His bony shoulders hunched against the evening chill, his eyes squinting against his tobacco smoke.

"West a' Bridger the country is passable good. Here's Bridger," he dug his stick in the ground, "an' here's that big butte west of there. You'll head west fer a spell an' at the Big Muddy River you'll take a southwesterly direction. You'll keep on thataway twenty miles an' you'll come to Sulphur Creek. A ways more, you'll cross the Bear." He tapped his stick on the mark for the river. "There's good trout in that river, if you have time to stop fer some. Then another five, six miles you go off to the northwest, twelve, fourteen miles more an' it's southwest fer twenty-five miles or so."

He punched the stick in the ground and stood up. "Then yer troubles are gonna start. Yer gonna say, now why didn' we listen to Clyman?"

"What troubles?"

"I been tellin' you. There's high mountains with a passel of canyons that're choked up with trees, brush, boulders, an' such like. The streams're filled with rocks an' there's places where there's cliffs on both sides."

"If there is a closer route, it is of no use to take a longer course," said Mr. Reed. "We trust that Mr. Hastings knows what he's about."

Mr. Clyman got up, his knees cracking as he straightened them out. "Uh-huh? Well, a man floats his own stick." Placing his hat on his head, he picked up his gun and nodded at the men. "Reed, Donner." He turned to Mother. "Thank ye kindly for the supper, ma'am. I'd best be gettin' on." He turned and walked off into the night.

Uncle Jacob stood up and threw his cold coffee on the fire. "Do you believe that? Fifteen thousand cattle on one ranch, an' that bein' one hundred and forty thousand acres? Thousands of acres of oats jes' growin' on their own? I think the man's a liar. We cain't put no stock in what he says."

The following day, Mother, Mr. New and Mr. Stanton went back to the Indian camp and Mother treated the boy's eyes.

"They were so encrusted that it took several washings before I could apply the medicine wash," she told us. "I asked Mr. New to tell

Blue Whirlwind that my power to cure came from fire and if the water was not boiled in the kettle over fire—I gave her one of my kettles—the medicine would have no power."

Mr. New looked at Mother quizzically. "Ma'am, why'd you tell her the water had to be boiled over fire? You don't believe in hocus pocus like they do."

"No. I couldn't be sure the water she used would be clean. I have found that when water is questionable, boiling before use seems to keep one from getting sick as often."

"Mother, what was the boy's name?"

"Little Elk."

June 27, 1846
My Dear Friend:

Two days ago we were at the outpost of Ft. Bernard, a trading post of very crude construction, situated seven or eight miles east of Fort Laramie. Here were encampments of the Sioux, one of the Ogallala led by Old Smoke, and two large villages of the Minneconjou Sioux. The plains surrounding the Fort are covered by their lodges, numbering perhaps two thousand.

They are a colorful and attractive people, one of the most powerful tribes in the country. Their standard of living is provided by the buffalo, as they use the skins and meat to trade for foodstuffs, blankets & other luxuries. Their conical-shaped tents are fashioned of buffalo skins & are remarkably adapted to their nomadic way of life. The hide covering is held in the conical shape by poles, tied at the top & spread in a circle at the bottom. When they break camp to travel, the tent is taken down & the poles are fastened to horses on each side with a framework supporting all their baggage. All of the work to make this happen is done by the women.

The road is lined with emigrants. A man returning east, a Mr. Wall, who stopped in our camp, has counted four hundred and ninety wagons. The companies have got along remarkably well. They have lost but a few head of cattle. A debate rages within our camp about the new route to the Salt Lake. I, for one, do not want to follow this new route. We have until Fort Bridger to make a decision.

I shall report again when the opportunity to post letters presents itself. We are now about 600 miles from Independence & about 1,400 miles from where we want to be.
Mrs. George Donner

We continued our journey, passing over the wild and desolate plain that surrounded the fort. We observed a cluster of scaffolds rising in the distance, with white objects scattered around on the ground. Mr. New, who traveled with us for awhile, told us that these constructions were Indian burials.

"These are some'a their dead chiefs. The Injuns think they'll be safe from desecration here, by the fort, but it's a fav'rite sport of the Crows when they comes through here to throw the bodies down and tear everythin' up, kind of like a slap in the face to the Sioux that're here. Those white objects you see are buffalo skulls—they arranges them in a circle on the ground below the scaffold, it has some kind of meanin'. They have all kinds of superstitions and mind ye, they're dead serious about it.

"The Crows're staying clear from here now, with all the Sioux around, but usually it's only the wretches that hang aroun' the fort that're here—too few to come out and defend their dead chiefs."

After we left Fort Laramie our progress became much slower. Our animals were considerably weakened by the travel and lack of good water and forage. Father chafed at the slow pace, knowing that we were falling behind the main emigration and the days of travel before the snow would close the pass of the Sierra Mountains were getting fewer.

On the third day, just after starting off after our noon stop, we were walking a distance away from the wagons when we noticed that the wagons had stopped. The air was so thick with dust we couldn't see what had stopped the train, and Mother became uneasy. She called to Elitha and Leanna who had wandered away.

"Girls, let's go back."

We were waiting for them to come up when we saw Father running to us. He was shouting and pointing to our wagons.

"What is it?" called Mother.

"Run!"

We could hear him now, and we started to run. As we got to him, he grabbed me up, Mother pulled Georgia along and yelled at Elitha to help Frances.

"Hurry! Get under the wagon!"

We could feel a throbbing in the air that turned into a shaking of the ground. People in the train were yelling and screaming. Father pointed to a huge brown cloud bearing down on us.

"Oh, my God. A buffalo stampede," Mother shouted. "They're going to come through the wagons."

The noise was incredible as the mass of huge beasts pounded toward us. A wagon was knocked over and the oxen swept under the thundering bodies. We scrambled under our wagon, choking from the dust, our hearts pounding from the run and fear. The ground shook violently. Our oxen were frantic, bucking and yanking in the bows, causing the wagon to jerk forward and sideways. We crawled on all fours to stay underneath.

A crazed buffalo ran between the wagon we were under and the next one, splintering the pole with a loud crack and rocking the wagon. The huge beast collapsed on its front legs only a few feet from us, bellowing horribly as it struggled to get up, pushing itself forward with its hind legs. Our oxen, now released, frantically pulled each other one way and then another, dragging part of the broken pole behind them.

It was a few minutes before we realized that the din was receding and the trembling of the ground had moved off. We heard gunshots and as we crawled out from beneath the wagon, we saw several of our company standing over the heaving and groaning buffalo that had run between the wagons.

"Broke his front legs on that pole, an' the pole's a goner, Mr. Donner," said Noah.

"Well, it could have been worse. We saw a wagon break up before they hit us. Let's see if we can help."

The men came back with bad news. The owner of the wagon had been killed while attempting to turn the beasts away. He left a wife who was feeble in health, a new-born babe and several children. The man was buried and the wife hired one of the single men to drive her wagon. They struggled on, only to be abandoned by the faithless driver, who took their rifle and made off to another wagon group in the vanguard of the company. Shortly thereafter, the poor woman became sick with a fever and died.

The children were now orphans, the eldest fourteen and the youngest only a few weeks old. The woman was buried by the side of the road and her children were parceled out amongst the emigrants.

"Oh, George, those little children, alone in the wilderness, their lives in the hands of strangers. I cannot bear the thought of something like that happening to us, leaving our children alone with strangers."

"They're bein' helped by people they know an' they'll take 'em on to Oregon."

We celebrated Independence Day at Beaver Creek, meeting up with many friends. We were quite surprised to find Mr. Bryant and Mr. Russell there. Mr. Bryant had stopped to await our party as he needed another man to fill out his company.

We feasted on buffalo meat, bread, beans, and greens. One of the ladies provided a pie made of sage hen and rabbit with a crust as light as a feather.

Toasts and speeches were made, punctuated by blasts from muskets. Mr. Bryant stopped by to speak with Father and Mother before starting out again.

"I hope that we will have the pleasure of your company in California before you return to the East," said Mother.

"I hope so too. Have you made your mind up on which route you will take?"

"George and I argue about it. It seems that the company is inclined to follow Mr. Hastings."

We saw the caravan of mules wending its way through the encampment. One man in the Bryant group had changed his mind and decided for Oregon, and Mr. Bryant persuaded one of our teamsters, Hiram Miller, to take his place. The mule train was much better handled now than it had been the first day they had set out from Fort Laramie. They'd had only a short instruction in managing and packing the mules and were barely away from the fort when they noticed that several of the packs were hanging under the bellies of the mules. We'd passed them on the road as they were struggling to re-pack and they suffered quite a bit of derision from some of our teamsters. It had been a subject of conversation at the campfire.

"The mules know more about the business than we do," said Mr. Bryant. "Several times I thought I could detect them giving a wink and a leer, as much as to say that if they could speak they would give us the benefit of their advice and instruction."

We lay by for two days to rest and repair and then we set out again toward the setting sun. As we traveled, we were passed by a steady stream of mounted Sioux warriors resplendent in war dress and paint.

Several of the braves came very close alongside our family wagon, looking at us, talking and gesturing and making us very nervous. We crossed to the side away from the Indians, but they continued along with the wagon, shouting and waving their shields and spears. Father came running up, taking his rifle off the rack on the wagon.

Mother stopped him. "George, it's the boy—Little Elk."

One of the fierce-looking braves had come close to us and in front of him on his horse was Little Elk. Mother walked over to them, her dress fluttering in the breeze, dust swirling as the ponies danced in impatience to be off. "I am glad your eyes are better," she called up to him. The boy grinned and pointed to his eyes. Then the braves nudged their horses with their knees and galloped off.

"I believe they was thankin' you for fixin' the boy's eyes," said Father.

"Yes, I think so too."

The caravan of Indians put the company on edge. Some of the warriors were very interested in Virginia Reed's pony. They gathered around, pestering her until Mr. Reed came up and made Virginia get in their wagon, handing the pony to one of the teamsters. This annoyed Virginia very much, because she enjoyed riding when the wagons were rolling.

She was annoyed more when the Indians swarmed around the Reed wagon to get a peek in the looking glass that hung outside. As she was fretting about being confined to the wagon she remembered how her father had startled some Indians by pulling out his field-glass with a loud click and pointing it in their direction. Virginia took the glass off its rack and whenever Indians would approach the wagon she took her revenge by scaring them with the field-glass.

We stopped for the night in a depression of a ridge we had climbed in early afternoon. As we were preparing our supper, an Indian man entered the camp. Letting fall his robes, he sat down beside the fire, followed by two or three others. They had with them their food bowls, and grunted in appreciation as Mother filled them with sweetened coffee. After we had eaten and the men had smoked, the Indians departed the camp.

"The older one, now," said Mr. New, "he has a standing in the tribe. He's proven himself by killin', being in battle, stealin' horses an' such like. That's why his face was painted black. He's killed a Pawnee an' taken a scalp. But those others, you noticed how they seemed bashful-like, an' kept back? They ain't distinguished themselves yet, an' they have no standin'. The Injun men're required to be great hunters, an' make war, or they can't achieve a place amongst the warriors of the tribe. An' the women requires it too. A brave without some honors is less of a man to the squaws."

"It is fascinating to observe their ways," said Mr. Stanton. "They have such a child-like nature."

"Injuns're as intrigued with the white man as the whites are with them. They're curious about things they can see an' somewhat comprehend, but they don't trouble themselves with what they can't—they just say it's 'medicine'. An Injun never has to worry himself with thinkin' things out."

"I observed," said Mother, "a family in our group being bothered by a group of Indian braves who crowded around them, most likely begging for something.

"The family was getting very vexed with these pests and the grandmother, for what reason I do not know, decided to remove her teeth, or by accident they fell out of her mouth. This resulted in a panic and the Indians fled, jabbering and holding their hands to their mouths in awe. But shortly their curiosity would get the better of them and they would slink back to observe her putting the teeth in and taking them out again, just to see the Indians falling over themselves trying to get away. But each time, they were compelled to return to see the mystery again. They thought she must surely be a powerful medicine woman."

Chapter Five

After leaving the Platte, we ascended some bluffs and traveled an arid plain.

The wagons inched along under clouds of brown dust, through a barren landscape. Most of the water we found had a terrible taste, and was bad for us and for the animals. There were more and more dead oxen on the trail and some alive but too exhausted to continue. As we walked past one dying cow, we stopped. She was too weak to lift her head, but rolled her eyes to us as we approached. There was a note pinned on her.

"Mother, what does the paper say?"

"That she is the best of cows, and she was left to die, but if anyone wants her they might have her."

"Can we take her? You can make her well."

"No, she is too far gone. There's nothing we can do but give her some water."

Mother knelt beside the cow, pouring water from her hand into the cow's mouth. The cow couldn't lift her head, but she managed to get a little of the water into her mouth with her tongue. Mother got to her feet. "She can't take enough to do any good. Let's pull that bush and put it over her head to shade her eyes. Then we must go on."

We reached a landmark called Independence Rock. Many of the

people in the train climbed on top, and some carved their names on the rock.

"We were led to believe this was some gigantic mountain, but it looks pretty small and tame," said Uncle Jacob. "I 'spected to see a rock so high you could hardly see its top."

We were now in the general vicinity of three other companies, sometimes ahead, sometimes behind. Our leaders were urging everyone to get an early start so we would be ahead and not have to suffer the dust of the other companies as well as our own. It was kind of a contest to see who would get out in front. But in this area the landscape permitted the trains to spread out to the sides to avoid some of the terrible dust.

We met the Sweetwater River and followed it, coming abreast of a cleft in the mountain wall that was called Devil's Gate. It was as wide as three wagons end to end, with high walls on each side of the stream flowing through it.

"There is an Indian legend regarding this point of interest," Mother told us at the campfire. "A Great Bad Spirit haunted this valley. He drove the buffalo before him, gorging himself upon them and the smaller game and drinking the streams and springs dry. He was in the shape of an enormous beast with huge tusks. He loosened huge rocks and sent them flying into the valley with his hind feet. He caused earthquakes when he roared and terrible winds with his breath."

"A prophet called upon the tribes to cease their warfare and cooperate in driving the beast from the valley. They combined forces and made a crusade against the Evil Spirit, attacking the beast with their arrows. The siege lasted many days until the body of the beast was full of arrows and he looked like a tremendous porcupine. The attack made him terribly angry and he stamped and snorted and then with his tusk he ripped a gap in the mountain. Through this gap the Great Bad Spirit disappeared."

The next day of travel was pleasant. The wagons creaked and

swayed over ground that was sometimes rolling, sometimes flat. We came upon throngs of insects resembling the cricket. They covered the road and the wagon wheels rolled over them making a crunching sound. They would fly against us, clinging to our clothes and hitting our faces, which made us shriek. Noah stopped the wagon and we got inside, giggling in relief to be away from the insects, but some flew into the wagon. Frances would catch them and pitch them out.

"When the wheels run over them it reminds me of back home, the crunching sound when our buggy went through snow," said Georgia.

The next night we were making ready for sleep when we heard a sound that was not part of the desert. At first it was soft and distant, then the sound grew louder and all heads turned when a horse and rider entered the campsite.

It was a young man by the name of Bonney, traveling east alone and bearing an open letter from Mr. Lansford Hastings directed to all emigrants on the road. The letter invited those bound for California to concentrate their numbers and strength and take a new route that he had explored. He wrote that the distance to California would be very much shortened.

"George," said Mr. Reed, "this is a practicable route for us. Time is getting short. It makes no sense to take a round-about course."

"Well, it might be. I'm going to reserve judgment until we meet up with Hastings and see how many wagons are going to take his lead."

"George," said Mother, "why take a chance on an unproven short-cut?"

"I expect we'll have plenty of time to decide."

"My family is going on Hastings's route," said Mr. Reed. "I see no advantage in going the longer way."

A number of people in our camp were sick and the cattle were suffering too. We saw more dead cattle along the road and one of our own went down and none of Mother's efforts could revive her.

Then our little mule, Willy, became weak and sick and could not continue. We were delayed a whole morning as Mother tried every remedy to help Willy.

We clustered around him, putting wet cloths on his head and body, patting him and begging him to get well, but it was all to no avail. He lifted his head and brayed, as if to say good-bye, and then he was gone.

"George," said Mother, "I am coming to believe that it is the toxic water that is causing so much illness. We've got to find water without this terrible mineral content."

"We can't go off for miles searchin' for water. We've just got to live with it."

"I believe the altitude has something to do with the sickness," said Mr. Reed. "A person not used to exertion at high altitudes must suffer some consequences as the body attempts to make an adjustment. Mountain men speak of this as mountain fever and say that once adjusted, sickness is rare."

"They seem never to suffer from illness an' a wound that would kill one'a us don't bother them," said Noah. "They's tough as hide leather, them boys. That mountain man, Smith, he cut his own leg off. He was shot by an Injun, breakin' the bones in his leg. There was nothing to do but cut 'er off, but nobody would do it, so he ups and does it hisself, an' lived to tell about it."

"You 'member that mountain man, the one that was mangled by a grizzly an' was left by his friends fer dead? He made it back to civilization after months of crawlin' through the wilderness, livin' off'n bugs an' rotten carcasses."

"Yep. Yer thinkin' of Hugh Glass. I reckon they get tough from livin' as a savage. An' wasn't Jim Bridger one a' the ones that left him fer dead?"

"I allow you're right. I heard that."

"You know," said Charles Stanton, "I have observed some of these mountain men and I notice the ease with which they lapse into being an Indian, yet the Indian does not easily become a white man."

"I mind what Zeb said about Injuns," said Solomon. "He said the way they live is better'n our's, all cooped up in a house an' never breathin' natural air, wearin' clothes that itch an' shoes that hurt yer feet."

"He's right about shoes," said Noah. "I traded fer some moccasins an' they did feel right good, 'til I stepped on one of them prickly pear thorns."

We saw more and more dead oxen along the road. They dropped from exhaustion and then were made quick meals of by the wolves. There were a great many wolves in the area and they were very bold. All night they kept up a wild chorus.

A man of the camp told a story about an encounter with a wolf the previous night. "I was supervisin' the watch," he said, "an' waitin' for my time to go on duty. I lay down an' covered myself with my blanket, but felt uncomfortable without somethin' to put my head on. So I looks around an' I find a slab of bacon in a sack an' I use that fer my pillow. I lay there fer a time, everythin' still. I guess I dozed some, when all at once the bacon leaves from under my head. I jumps up an' I seen this big wolf backin' off, pullin' the sack of bacon, stoppin' every once in awhile an' growling. I was afeered a' shootin' at him bein' inside camp but I draws my knife an' swipes at him. I didn't get my knife in him, but he dropped the bacon an' run off."

I had frightening dreams about wolves. I awoke in fear and cried for Mother, begging her to sleep with us in the wagon instead of the tent.

Finally she climbed into the wagon and squeezed in beside the three of us. In a few days we left the area where there were so many wolves and my fear lessened.

"Soon we will be on the crest of the Rocky Mountains," said Mother. "From there on, the streams will be running west."

"How long have we been gone from home?" Frances asked.

"Hmm. Let me think. Today is July 19. It's been about three months, about half our journey."

"You mean we have *three more months to go?*" groaned Elitha. "I'm sick of this. The dirt, the dust, eating on the ground. The water's terrible and I'm tired of eating biscuits and beans and bacon—"

"Are you sick of the dancing and singing and merriment with all your friends at night?"asked Leana. "And all that sparking from Charles and Laon—"

"What sparkin'?" asked Father.

"Leanna, hush up!" said Elitha.

"You had some of the berry pie, and two helpings of the wild onion stew—"

"It gave me the trots," whined Elitha.

"Yeah, me too, 'Litha," said Father. "But the life we'll have in California will make up for these little discomforts. Mother, that a letter to back home?"

"Yes, I am writing a letter to Mr. Francis to publish in the newspaper. I wish I'd had it ready to send when that young man, Mr. Bonney, came through. Who knows when another opportunity will present itself."

"Well, you can leave it at Ft. Bridger. I 'spect that there'll be someone to take it back east," said Father.

July 19, 1846
My Dear Friend:

We've left the Sweetwater River & ascended the dividing ridge of South Pass. There was a misconception that we would have a difficult passage through the South Pass of the Rocky Mountains, but this was not so. The gap in the mountains is many miles in breadth & the ascent very gradual. After two or three miles of travel over a level surface, the trail descended to a spring known as Pacific Spring .

We are now into an arid undulating plain covered by wild sage. In front of us there are many buttes and strange formations rising

above the plain. We have traveled about three hundred miles since Fort Laramie.
Mrs. George Donner

We camped on the Little Sandy and here we were joined by the nine members of the Breen family. With them was their friend Mr. Dolan. Mr. Dolan was always full of fun and laughter. Mr. Breen was a thin man and always a little hunched as though he had a hurt inside. Oft times at the evening campfire he would play the violin and Mr. Dolan would dance a jig and they would talk of life in Ireland, their home country.

The wagons going to Oregon turned off near the Little Sandy. Others who had already decided they would not chance taking the route of Mr. Hastings to California turned off here too. The parting of new and old friends was sad.

It was cold at night and in the mornings we had ice in our water buckets. One morning, as the wagons began to move, we pulled around a stopped wagon and saw a woman on the side of the road wailing. The woman was holding her children, refusing to continue. Mother and Aunt Betsey tried to help, but the woman's mind was deranged and nothing could be done for her. Then some men came up, picked up the children, put them in the wagon and the husband drove off, leaving the woman sitting there.

"Her husband's at the end of his rope dealin' with her craziness," said Father.

"That poor soul!" exclaimed Aunt Betsey. "She came to my camp last night, talkin' crazy, walkin' around like she didn't know where she was. I know what set her off. They was travelin' with her folks an' her daughter's family, an' they'd all decided for Oregon an' turned off to Fort Hall this mornin', but the woman's husband said no, he was goin' to California. She couldn't bear to part with her daughter an' the little granddaughter an' the rest of her folks. She jes' went to pieces."

As we approached the evening camp we saw a wagon burning, the same family of the left-behind wife. There were several men helping to put out the blaze so we went on, looking for a good spot away from the crowd. That evening Father reported the news about the unfortunate family.

"That woman got up, cut across the country, an' when her husband came up she tol' him she'd knocked her oldest child in the head with a rock when he'd come back to get a horse. The man believed her a'course—she'd been acting so strange—so he took off to go back an' find the boy. When he left she set fire to the wagon."

"Was the boy hurt badly?" Mother asked.

"No, he hadn't even seen his ma."

"She's likely goin' to come to her senses now or get another floggin', said Uncle Jacob.

"I know somethin' of how that woman feels," said Aunt Betsey. "Her husband tol' her they'd be with her family so's she'd agree to go an' then he ups an' takes off for California instead."

"If'n he decides a thing, it's the duty of his wife to go along with it without makin' a fuss an' causin' trouble for him. I'd do the same thing," said Uncle Jacob.

Aunt Betsey glared at him. "You just try an' not keep your word to me, Jacob Donner. I'd do more than burn your wagon."

Mr. Stanton came to talk to Father. "Sir, it's necessary that a captain be elected and most of us feel that you are the best qualified."

"Most venerable, perhaps," replied Father, "but qualified, no. That post requires a man that don't care about bein' nice to people, that can hold himself away from formin' friendships."

The company insisted that Father should be their captain and he finally agreed. Mother was upset. "George, you said—"

"An' at the time I meant it. But who do you think could take the job? James would be a good leader but the people don't like him an' most likely wouldn't take direction from him. He'll share responsibility."

July 28, 1846.

Fort Bridger is just a small trading post established by Mr. Bridger and his partner, Mr. Vasquez. It consists of two or three crude log structures. It is in a beautiful setting in a fertile valley. When we arrived we were surprised and disheartened to learn that Mr. Hastings had already departed with a train of more than sixty wagons, leaving word for late arrivals to follow in the wagon tracks of the group.

We inquired of people at the fort as to the feasibility of this route that Hastings is advocating and were told that we will find an abundant supply of wood, water, and pasturage along the whole line of road, with only one dry drive of thirty or forty miles.

Mrs. George Donner

We remained at the fort three days, the men making repairs and the women catching up on washing and cleaning some of the accumulated dirt and useless baggage from the wagons.

When most of the work was done, we sat by the wagon, enjoying the respite. Mother had taken out her rocking chair and was writing in her journal. A warm breeze rustled the leaves in the big cottonwood tree overhead and fragrance wafted from the grasses and flowers that carpeted the meadow. Mother waved away a persistent fly, finally stunning it with a quick swipe of her fan.

"At least we're not besieged by gnats like we had at the camp last night," she murmured. "I should get those berry pies started, but it's so pleasant, it's making me sleepy."

We were startled as we heard and felt the flap of wings as a huge crow lit on the ground in front of us. It side-stepped, first one way and then the other, all the while fixing us with its yellow eyes.

"Hello. You're a tame one." As Mother spoke, two more crows, smaller in size, flapped down, twisting their heads around as if questioning what was going on. I tossed a piece of biscuit that I had in the pocket of my apron in front of the big crow, but he didn't seem interested. He just kept looking at Mother, opening his beak and closing it, like he wanted to talk. Mother jumped up and shook her apron at the crows.

"Get away! Get away!"

We were as startled as the crows, who flew off into the top of the tree. Shakily, Mother picked up her journal that had fallen to the ground and sat back down. I went to her and sat on her lap.

"Mama, why did you yell at the crows?"

"They gave me a bad feeling, like an omen—I don't like to speak of it. It's just that it reminds me of when my other children and my first husband, Mr. Dozier, were buried. Look, my journal is all dusty."

I took the journal and jumped off Mother's lap, shaking the pages to get the dirt out.

"We don't usually see many crows around here."

We looked for the sound of the voice and saw a man approaching us. "I 'spect they're lookin' for leavin's from the wagon train. Are ye writin' a journal, missus?"

"Yes. I haven't been as faithful to it lately as I ought to be. I'm Mrs. George Donner, and these are my daughters. What is your name?"

"Goodyear, ma'am. I be Miles Goodyear."

"Do you live here at the fort?"

"Yes'm. I'm a trader."

"Oh, yes. I think my husband traded one of our cows to you for an ox. She'll be a good milker again, I'm sure."

Mr. Goodyear raised his arm and pointed to a patch of growth about a quarter mile away. "I wondered if'n you might be interested in writin' in yer journal that in yonder willow thicket a man by the name a' Black was killed by a band a' fifty Blackfoot Injuns. He defended hisself bravely an' even bein' wounded, he killed a passel 'fore they overcame him. That's how it is in the mountains, ye takes yer chances."

We gasped. "Are those Indians still here?"

"Oh, not anymore, little girl. That was a long time ago. Mostly they come to trade, and if they caused mischief Mr. Bridger wouldn't trade with them."

"Mr. Goodyear, do you know anything of the route Mr. Hastings is advocating?" asked Mother.

"Ma'am, it's mighty rough country. Hastings has been through there an' he led some fifty or sixty wagons out a few days ago. There ain't no road, but with all them wagons makin' a road it most likely won't be difficult for those who follow. There's some bad desert to cross, but if yer animals're in good condition, you might make it through without too many of 'em dyin' on you. Mr. Bridger's wantin' to have a road opened 'cause trade's been mighty slow since most of the emigrants been takin' Greenwood's cut-off. Ma'am, there's a young man by the name of John Baptiste that's been stayin' with me. He's anxious to join up with a family goin' to California. He's got no means of goin' hisself."

"He will have to talk with my husband. We have already agreed to take Mr. Halloran with us. I don't know if Mr. Donner will want to take responsibility for anyone else."

"That's mighty fine of you. The people he was with left him here at the post 'cause the consumption's about got him. Truthfully, I can't see the man lastin' much more'n a few days."

"I am afraid that you are right," replied Mother.

That evening the children were put to bed and the people gathered at our fire. Mother put an extra blanket over us and a heavy shawl around her shoulders before she left the wagon.

"I want to listen to what they're saying," said Frances. She lifted the canvas cover so we could peek out.

"Me too, move over," said Georgia. I wiggled between them. We could see the fire glowing, dying and glowing again as the wind played with it. The orange light flickered on the solemn faces of those gathered around. Father was talking.

"Y'all know there's sixty wagons ahead of us breakin' the trail, led by this Hastings fellow. Time is gettin' short an' this here route may cut many days off our travel. The men here at the fort say there's a forty-mile section without water, but with good plannin' we can overcome that."

"Clymer was against it in no uncertain terms," said Mr. Stanton.

Mr. Denton spoke up. "That other bloke that came through, the one that had been with Mr. Frémont, he spoke unfavorably of the route too."

"Sublette? I heard he tol' Cap'n Davis the southern way of goin' was the same miles as goin' north an' had sixty miles of desert."

"No. It warn't Sublette."

"You must be speakin' of Joe Walker," said Noah. "He's the man that's drivin' those horses through from California. You know, it's said of him that he don't follow trails, he *makes* 'em. Walker thinks that Mr. Hastings wants men to fight in California for independence from Mexico. He says independence will likely raise the value of the land, makin' Hastings a sight of money."

"Walker's a puke and a thief, stole those horses from the Mexicans. You can't trust what a man like that says," someone exclaimed.

"Walker's well thought of an' there's lots of good folk from Missouri," countered Noah.

"Now, let's keep to the subject," said Father. "Hastings *is* openin' this route an' we can follow him. It's already late in the season an' we still have more'n a thousand miles to go."

Mother stood up. "If we go the old route we'll still arrive at the peak of the California Mountains in mid-October. Everyone we ask about the new route is against it, except for these men at the fort, and of course, Mr. Hastings. And their motives are questionable. Why take a chance on the unproven?"

"No offense, Mrs. Donner, but these matters are best left up to the men," said Mr. Reed. "There is said to be a savings of three to four hundred miles and on this route we won't have the terrible dust since there are but sixty wagons ahead of us."

"It would be good to get away from the dust," agreed Mr. Foster.

"We're so far behind," said Mother, "that even if we go north we'll be days behind the other wagons and their dust."

Mr. Reed made a gesture of exasperation. "If we take the new route, I think we can make Sutter's fort in seven weeks."

"Whoopee! Only seven more weeks!" exclaimed Mr. Pike. "I'm all for that! No more eatin' dust, dyin' from thirst an' all the other things we been findin' so intolerable. Mother Murphy, what do you think?"

"I'm all fer cuttin' off some distance. Our animals are about to give out an' we're short on provisions."

"Aye, it hae the ring of reason," said Mr. Breen. "With yon party makin' the road, we'll not have the problem gettin' through the mountains that Mr. Clyman spoke of. I have provisions enough, but a shortnin' of the journey would be welcome."

Father stood up. "Y'all make your decision. The Donner an' Reed wagons will follow Mr. Hastings."

The group left our campfire. Father poured the last of the coffee on the embers of the dying fire. Mother didn't get up, and Father went to her and gently pulled her up into his arms. Mother was small, barely five feet, and Father was over six feet. The top of her head was way short of Father's chin.

"I feel so strongly that we are making a mistake, George. My heart tightens and I have a sense of doom."

"Honey, we've made the best decision."

"Why take the chance?"

"I respect your feelin's, lots of times you're right. But every person here thinks it's the thing to do. I take that into account."

The young man that Mr. Goodyear had told us about came to our camp. He carried a few things in a rolled-up Indian blanket and was dressed in ill-fitting mountaineer's clothing. He told Mother that his father had been a fur trapper.

"And your mother?"

"*Mi Mamá*, she was of the Pueblo of Taos, a Spanish lady who marry the *Anglo, Señora.* As a boy I live in Taos, where most of the people speak the *Español.* I know a little of the French too. I know the language of the Indians who call themselves Utah an' I have the sign language for others that live in the mountains an' deserts that you must cross. I can be of much use to you."

"Do you know the country south and west of here?"

"No, *Señor*, I no travel that country. I no think it a good idea, but if that is the way you will go, I want to go with you. I will have trust in *Dios, Señor.*"

Father chuckled. "And I guess we will too. What's your name, son?"

"I am called Juan Baptiste Trudeau. I say it the Spanish way, but you may say John. Is all the same."

"How old are you?"

"I have sixteen years, *quizas* seventeen. *Mi Abuela*, she lost the count. I am a man, *Señor.*"

Juan said that he had been with Kit Carson and Captain Frémont on their expedition to California, but had left the group at the headwaters of the Green River. He'd come to Fort Bridger determined to join one of the wagon parties.

Another young man, Antonio, attached himself to the company at Ft. Bridger. Mr. Stanton was still with us, and there were several families that had joined us along the road between the Greenwood Cut-Off and Ft. Bridger. Mr. Eddy, with a wife and two small children; a widow woman, Mrs. Murphy, with five children and two married daughters with their husbands and children. Also with us was Mr. McCutcheon from Missouri, his wife and baby daughter. There were several that our group called "the Dutchmen" because they were of German heritage: There was Mr. Keseberg, his wife, and two children, a man named Wolfinger and his wife, and four single men: Charlie Burger; Mr. Spitzer; Mr. Reinhardt; and Mr. Hardcoop.

Chapter Six

Our wagons left Ft. Bridger following the tracks of the company led by Lansford Hastings.

The sun was warm and a breeze flittered the leaves in the cottonwoods along the creek as our wagons followed the road out from Fort Bridger.

We ascended from the valley, traveling to the left of a high butte. Here the road forked, the right-hand road the old trail that went north to Fort Hall.

We stood there for a few minutes with Mother as the wagons rolled past, the dust billowing in clouds. She gazed off into the distance, arms crossed.

"Mother! The wagons are leaving us."

She turned. "Well, I guess we can't walk to California by ourselves, can we? Come along, girls, it's a fine day, let's enjoy it."

Not too far from Fort Bridger one of the Breen boys suffered a broken leg. He and Patty Reed were running their ponies when his horse stepped into a hole and took a hard fall. Edward was thrown to the ground and knocked senseless, his leg broken. We ran to tell Mother of Eddie's accident and she hurried to the Breen wagons.

"We sent back to the fort for someone who could help," said Mr. Breen.

They moved Eddie into some shade by the wagon and Mother gave him willow bark to chew to ease the pain. After a long time a bearded mountain man appeared riding a mule.

"How'ye. They call me Jim," he said.

Edward's mother didn't like the looks of the mountain man. Her voice was shaky. "Mister, hae you experience in doctorin' a break like this? Hae you any surgical trainin'?"

"Har! Surgical trainin'? A'course I have." Jim spit a stream of tobacco juice that splatted on the dusty ground. "I've killed an' skinned out mebbe a hunnert buffler an' as many deer, to say nothin' of all t'other game. I've done more cuttin' on animals an' folks than nine out'a ten surgeons. I've cut arrows out'a people many times an' cleaned up bad wounds a'one kind or 'nother. I opine I've more experience than any ye so-called doctors."

He unrolled a bundle wrapped in canvas and took out a saw and a long-bladed knife. "Let's git 'em up on a wagon gate. Do ye got any whiskey?"

Eddie commenced to pitch a fit as the man approached him with his tools. "Let me be! Ma, no!"

Someone brought a flask of spirits and Jim took it, draining most of the bottle. Then he put the flask to Eddie's mouth. "Here, young'un, it'll hep ye stand the cuttin'."

Eddie became frantic, begging not to have his leg taken off. "Ma, get him away from me!"

Finally, not having any confidence in this rough-looking fellow, Mr. Breen gave Jim five dollars and sent him back to the Fort, stiff with indignation that he wasn't allowed to demonstrate his skills.

"Margaret," said Mother, "I have a medicine for broken bones. I'll be back in a few minutes."

By the time Mother returned Mr. Breen had made splints. Mother smoothed some greasy stuff on Edward's leg.

"This is made from a root that an Indian healer gave to me. Eddie, try to stay calm. We'll straighten your leg and bind it up. Keep chewing on that bark."

"Is it gonna hurt?"

"Yes, but perhaps not a lot. I was told the salve will relax your leg. You might even become sleepy."

We edged up. "Eddie, does it hurt a lot?"

His face was streaked where tears had washed away dirt. "It's not so bad." He turned his head and looked around. "Is he gone?"

"Your mother sent him away. Our mother is a healer," said Georgia. "She'll help you."

Soon Mother said all was ready to straighten his leg. "Girls, go back to our wagons and tell Father we need to make camp."

When Mother returned she told us of Eddie's treatment. "It's fortunate that the bone had not broken through the skin. It was painful for him, but easier than I expected. "

"Do you think we can move on tomorrow?" asked Father.

"Yes. They've placed Edward on a hammock arrangement in their wagon. He'll be jostled some, but he's fairly comfortable."

Edward suffered for a time with the jolting and jerking, but in a few days he could sit up and in a month he was riding his horse again.

Baptiste was walking with us when we reached a place where we saw two lodge poles lying on the ground. "*Señora* Donner, a company of Shoshone Indians, they go this way. They were in much hurry."

"How do you know?"

"You see the poles for the lodges? The poles no easy to find an' they have much value. The Indians they move fast, their soldiers no let them stop for the poles that drop off from the travois. You see the dung of their horses? It is much scattered an' that means the horses are moving fast. I think they get away from other Indians. The people they move with all the village, the women an' children an' the old ones."

"How can you tell they are Shoshone?"

"I see the tracks of moccasins. Each kind of Indian, they have ways of doing things. The way they make the moccasins, even so."

Juan Baptiste turned to us. "Little ones, do you know the hand talk for the Snake Indians?" Baptiste moved his right hand in an up and down waving motion. "See, it is like a snake moving. If I want to tell you that I saw a Snake Indian, I do this." He placed two fingers outward from his eyes. "You see, *niñas*? I know something more. Soon we are going to have rain."

Frequently we were bothered by squalls of rain and when the clouds lifted, we could see snow on the mountains. Sometimes during the rain we would ride in the wagon and Mother would write in her journal.

August 5, 1846

After leaving Ft. Bridger we crossed the Little Muddy and camped in a valley covered with fine grass & occasional clumps of cottonwood trees & willows. We lost the road & descended into a narrows enclosed by high yellow & red cliffs. At the end of the hollow we came to an impassable barrier of red sandstone & had to reverse our track to find the road again. We ascended a high elevation on our left, passing over a plain with sage so thick it was difficult to force our way through.

We traveled over ridges where the western slopes were abrupt and precipitous. The wagons were eased down, skittering and bumping over the rough terrain, rocks and dirt bouncing down the slope. Then we clattered and jolted over the rocks littering the floor of the canyon. Red cliffs towered over us, and the sounds of people talking, the blows of hammers, and the clatter of hooves would echo back and forth.

After making our way out of the canyon, we followed the trail along the side of a stream for several miles and then the lead wagons halted. Father went to see what had stopped the wagons.

"This paper was stuck in a bush," said Mr. Eddy.

"Here, let me have it," said Mr. Reed. He read what was written, then slapped the paper against his palm in frustration. "It's from Hastings. He's telling anyone that comes through here not to follow him."

"What? That can't be. We don't know any other way to go."

"He's saying the canyon will be too difficult for us," said Mr. Reed, "and he says to send a messenger ahead to find him. He'll return and show us a better route. We'll have to decide on a course of action."

It was determined that Mr. Reed, Mr. Pike and Mr. Stanton would go ahead on horseback to find Mr. Hastings.

We expected that they would return soon, but the days dragged on with no sign of them. In the afternoon on the fifth day some of the children came running.

"A horseman's coming! It's not one a' our horses, but the man's wearin' a hat like Mr. Reed wears."

It was Mr. Reed. We gathered around.

"Where're the other two men?" asked Father.

"Their horses gave out. They'll meet up with us."

Mrs. Reed brought water for her husband and he drank some, then poured the rest over his head, drying his face with a handkerchief.

Squatting down on his heels, he began to draw lines in the dust with a stick. "This is about where we are and this is the Salt Lake. Between here and there is a maze of canyons. They're steep, rocky, and filled with growth." Mr. Reed drew several wavy lines. "This canyon here is the one they took." He tapped the stick on the second line. "This is the one Hastings pointed out to me—the one I followed back."

He stood up stiffly. "We followed where Hastings' company went through the canyon. We could see where they had so much trouble. That canyon is just barely wide enough to get by on the side of the river, in places they were into the river. They had to move huge boulders and many times had to fill in with rocks and brush."

"I don't understand why we can't follow 'em. The road's made now," said Father.

"Well, what they could do and we cannot is pull up the steep cliffs," replied Mr. Reed. "They had to winch up the wagons. We don't have enough men to do it. Even so, they lost one of their wagons and two oxen over a precipice. Look, if you men want to go on up by horse-back and look it over—"

"No! We've been sitting here for five days. We haven't the time," said Mr. Eddy.

"Hastings pointed out to me the way he thought we should go, he wouldn't come back all the way. I blazed the trail so we could find it again. We can go back and take the Fort Hall route or we can proceed. I feel we have no choice but to go ahead."

Uncle Jacob gave a bitter snort. "We shouldn't've hitched our wag-on to that no-good Hastings."

"We need to talk this over." Father raised his voice so everybody could hear. "Y'all get supper, then come back to my wagons."

They gathered around our campfire. There was a mournful feeling to the meeting. Aunt Betsey leaned towards Mother. "I'm reminded of people gathered around a body waiting for the preacher to begin," she whispered.

"I recommend we proceed," said Mr. Reed. "It will be hard work, but with every man doing their part we can get through. The work can be accomplished in a week or two, and we will then pick up the trail of Hastings' company."

Hot arguments and purple recriminations circled the campfire, but finally everybody agreed to proceed.

The men hacked tunnels through the dense thickets, heaving the wagons over gullies and through riverbeds thick with boulders. It was a maze of canyons, at times leading to dead-ends. Wagons would be pulled up inclines and over ridges, only to face more ridges on the other side.

Mr. Reed came one evening to talk with Father. "We've got to get everyone to do a fair share of this work. Those Dutchmen aren't working a full day. Today Burger stayed behind after the noon break. Then Wolfinger left the work detail and then Reinhardt."

"Burger's hurting bad from that big rock that rolled on him yesterday. It's fortunate he didn't have a broken leg. Hardcoop is old an' weak. He can't walk more'n a mile or two before he gives out. Reinhardt now, I reckon he could do more."

"There's Spitzer," replied Mr. Reed. "He worked for a couple of hours yesterday and today he lay in camp. There are several others that aren't pulling their weight, George. Everybody's got to pitch in. Jacob sits down more than he works."

"Jacob is a sick man," said Mother, "but still he works as much as he's able. Betsey, her boys and I and our two older girls have been working. You could send Baylis and Eliza to help. They can do something."

"Baylis can't work in the daytime, afflicted like he is with his white skin. He does his share standing guard at night. Eliza has to help my wife. Margaret can't be expected to do the cooking and chores."

"Perhaps Virginia could help Margaret with the chores. That would free Eliza to work," said Mother.

Mr. Reed looked annoyed. "Women should not do this kind of work."

Father tried to smooth things over. "Tamsen, the men'll get it done. There's no call for the women to work. I'll go talk to those men."

"I'll go with you," said Mr. Reed. "It's about time they learn they have to do their share."

"James, I think it's best if you don't. There seems to be some hard feelin's between you an' them."

"I've done nothing to—"

Father wearily held up his hand. "James, let me do this. I'm too tired to argue."

"George, we'll go with you," said Mother. "We can visit with Mrs. Keseberg."

The German men were eating supper in company with Mrs. Keseberg and Mrs. Wolfinger. "Greetings, Donner, Mrs. Donner," said Mr. Keseberg.

We sat down with the two women and Father sat down on a stump. He cleared his throat. "Well, it's been a back-breakin' job gettin' through these canyons an' we ain't there yet. There's a lot more work ahead of us an' we're goin' to have to put in extra effort. Each one is goin' to have to do his share the best that he's able.

"Now, Burger's hurtin' from yesterday, needs to lay off a day or two. Mr. Hardcoop, we don't expect you to do heavy work, you're too weak. Wolfinger, I ain't complainin', you did what you could. Spitzer, you didn't work at all today an' Reinhardt, you quit early."

Mr. Keseberg started to get up, but Father quickly held up his hands, palms out. "Keseberg, you been pullin' your weight. Nobody's sayin' you ain't."

"You expect us to work harder than the others?" Mr. Keseberg was angry. "Some of those teamster men, they're not working full out. And who gave Reed the job of boss-man? He can do some of the hard work."

"Let's not get into petty bickerin'. I'll be talkin' to the rest of the men too. All we want is for everyone to do their share, best they can." Father looked around the group. "What do you say?"

"Ve vill verk, but Reed and the others have to do the same verk as us," said Mr. Reinhardt.

We returned to our camp and Father went to talk to the other men. When he came back, he leaned against the wagon and watched Mother kneading bread.

"I'll bake this tonight and share it around in the morning. How did it go in the other camps?"

"They're all sour as can be, but they'll do the best they can. I just wish we had more men."

"James's attitude bothers me, George. He acts as if he's ordering his own workers around. He reminds me of a slave owner thinking about using his whip."

"We're all on a short fuse."

"George, I wonder if you couldn't use the oxen to pull some of that thick brush out."

"Uproot the stuff with chains? Might take more time than choppin', but we could try it."

"Well, some of that brush might be shallow rooted and pop right out."

"Yeah, mebbe so. I'll talk to the men, see what they think."

Father gathered the teamsters and they worked out how they might use the oxen to pull out the brush and trees. The next morning the work group gathered.

"We're gonna try draggin' the big clumps out using a team," Father announced. "We'll use our men to chain an' drive the oxen. The rest of you work on clearin' what we can't pull out."

"Vere iss Reed? He iss not verking?" asked Mr. Reinhardt.

"He's comin'," said Milt. "I see him saddlin' up over yonder now."

Father turned to Noah. "You get the oxen started. The rest of you start on over. I'll be along."

Father walked over to talk to Mr. Reed, who was already mounted on his horse. Mother wanted us to stay at the wagon but we begged to go, promising not to get in the way. The group straggled behind Noah and the oxen to where work had stopped the day before. In a few minutes Father and Mr. Reed came up.

"Looks like Reed got off his horse," murmured Uncle. "I wonder that the man can walk."

"All right," called out Father, "let's try it there."

He pointed to a clump of twisted and gnarled growth and Noah coaxed the oxen into position. Father squatted down to get a better view of the work. "Jim, couple more times, okay? That'll do 'er."

When everybody was standing clear, Father signaled for Noah to start the oxen.

The beasts, tired and poorly as they were, did their best. They strained and scrabbled around on the rocks for a minute or two and then the roots of the clump began tearing from the ground. The oxen bounded forward as the clump gave way, flinging a thick cloud of dust in the air.

"Whoa! Whoa there!" shouted Noah.

Father waved his arm and the men moved in and began to drag the big clump out of the way. The rest of the group began clearing rocks and smaller growth. Frances helped carry branches and small rocks, but Mother made Georgia and me sit under a scrub tree where she thought we would not be in harm's way.

The canyon was beastly hot and there was no cooling breeze. The sun was almost directly overhead when Noah called to Father. "Mr. Donner, I think we need to get another team. These oxen have quit on us."

"Yeah," replied Father, "it's about time to rest anyways. Denton an' I looked over the next section. There's a place where there's big rocks, but not as much thicket. This afternoon we'll only need a few of the strongest men. We'll work on movin' those rocks. Everyone else can rest up."

"Oh, thank God," said Aunt Betsey. She held her hands out. "Look at these blisters on my hands, an' my back's so sore I cain't straighten myself."

As the tools were gathered we heard angry voices. It was the German men, pushing their way through Mr. Reed's group which was ahead of them.

"Iss goot you join the peasants to verk today, Reed," said one. "Oh, iss pity, you haf got your boots dirty."

Mr. Reed turned around. "Who said that?"

No one answered. Mr. Reed stood with his feet spread, hands tight in fists. "Are you afraid to speak to my face?"

The German men went on as we approached. Father put his hand on Mr. Reed's shoulder.

"There ain't no call to get upset, James."

"He's right, Mr. Reed," said Milt. "Those Dutchmen ain't worth spit. They ain't worth gettin' riled up about."

Mr. Reed wiped the sweat and dirt off his face with a handkerchief. "I'll not be braced again."

That afternoon some of the children came running to tell of wagons coming. We saw a tall, raw-boned man with a shambling walk and a face of leather coming up ahead of three wagons.

"We was afeared we weren't gonna catch up with you people," he called. "We was tol' back at Bridger you were a week or more ahead. I'm Franklin Graves, from Marshall County, Illinois."

Mr. Graves had a large family; his wife, Elizabeth and nine children, including a married daughter and her husband, Mr. Fosdick. Teamstering for them was John Snyder. They had intended for Oregon, but changed their minds at Fort Bridger.

The backbreaking task continued, a little easier now with the men of the Graves family added to the work force. A section of road would be made, a mile or two or three, and then the wagons would be brought up and we would camp again. In one canyon our wagons crossed a stream nineteen times in five miles.

The land rose steadily, the trees becoming larger. We ascended a high ridge where we could see far off, over lower mountains, the valley of the Great Salt Lake. At last! But there was still a lot of country to cross and it was rough country. We rattled and jerked down the other side of the ridge, bridging a steep ravine by filling it with trunks of trees and brush.

At the foot of the mountain we came to a stream and here the Reed family wagon suffered a broken axle. Mrs. Reed and little Tommy were tumbled around in the wagon, but they suffered only a little bruising.

"I'm surprised it's held up this long," said Mr. Eddy. "I told him back in Independence he should have a jointed pole. He has no spare?"

"No, we'll have to make one."

"Why are we stopped?" Mr. Reed had just come up. He'd been riding ahead scouting the area. With him was Mr. Stanton and Mr. Pike, the men who days ago had gone with Mr. Reed to find Mr. Hastings.

"Sure am glad to see you men," said Father. "You look pretty drug out."

"We were just about to kill my horse for food when Reed came on us," said Mr. Stanton.

"Go on to my wagons an' Mrs. Donner will give you somethin' to eat. We'll be along after we figure out what to do with this broken axle. We sure want to hear what you have to tell us."

Mr. Reed dismounted and squatted down to look at the damage.

"James," said Father, "Eddy here's a coachmaker an' has offered to help make a new axle. Others will help, too. Send your men to scout for a tree."

"Where is my wife? My children?"

"They're with Mrs. Donner in our wagon, they're all right," said Father.

"Milt," ordered Mr. Reed, "take care of my horse and put my saddle on the dun. We'll leave after I've seen to my wife."

"Yes, sir. I'll do 'er. Some of the others'll help, there's no need for you to go."

Mr. Reed swung around and yelled at Milt. "Do what I told you!"

Milt stood for a moment with a shocked look on his face, then led the horse away. After a moment Mr. Reed headed down the line of wagons.

"Seems he's swallowed a prickly pear," said Father. "Mr. Eddy, let's commence an' get that axle off."

At the campfire that evening, Mr. Stanton and Mr. Pike told a harrowing tale of getting lost and almost giving up hope of finding us.

"No telling where we were nor where you might be," said Stanton, "but we do know that we can't get to the valley by the direction you're heading now. We have to backtrack and cross over another ridge."

"The hell you say! We saw the valley from atop that mountain we just came over. We figured this here stream would take us to it."

Everyone was disheartened. More thickets, streams, and boulders. More hacking and chopping. The men were exhausted, at the limits of their endurance. The company struggled on. Six long days, another ridge topped and descended.

We came out into a meadow that led into another canyon and beyond was the valley of the Great Salt Lake. Camp was made for the night and men went to survey this last canyon. The news was not good.

"The canyon's choked with growth, thick as what we done come through, mebbe worse."

It was too much. The company could not face more hard labor, so it was decided to go over the ridge. The first wagon was triple-teamed and the pull up the sheer face of the canyon wall began.

"There's a powerful right chance the oxen'll slip and go over," said Mr. Graves. "Some of us better get hold of those yokes an' give 'em a hand."

The men chocked the wheels after every few feet and the oxen were prodded to their limits, but the wagon began slipping.

"Hey, you there, Smith! Stick some more wood under those wheels!" yelled Father.

"It ain't a'workin', Mr. Donner. We've got to have more oxen to pull."

"Yeah, we'll have to hitch up more teams."

It was a terrible struggle, but all the wagons were taken over the hill and at last we descended to the valley of the Great Salt Lake.

Chapter Seven

We were out of the Wasatch Mountains,

but now we faced a terrible desert.

The delay of waiting for Mr. Reed to return, the strenuous work, and the worry that provisions were going to run out had taken a toll on the group. Each day the cursing and bad talk increased and quarreling was a daily occurrence.

We hurried on, and at last we came across the trail of the wagons led by Mr. Hastings. Mr. Halloran's consumption had become much worse in the days we were in the mountains and he died a few days after reaching the valley. Mother had done all she could for him. He was buried with full Masonic rites conducted by Mr. Reed.

The road led off in a northerly direction, then bent around the point of a mountain leaving the lake off to our right. We passed into an area where there were many natural wells filled with cold pure water.

The next day we made a long drive and camped where there were more wells and good grass. The trail swept off to the west along what must have been a beach from a vanished lake high above the present.

After another long drive through a sagebrush plain, we came to a good meadow and it was here we found shreds of a note that had been mounted on a board but had been torn apart by birds. The scraps were collected and everyone gathered around as Mother sat down with the board on her lap and pieced them together.

"It's not complete, but from what I can make out the note was written by Mr. Hastings. It says we have a desert crossing ahead—two days and two night's—no water."

"Our oxen are in terrible shape," wailed Mrs. Murphy. "We can't get through without water."

"We'll fill every container we have. There's good grass here, we'll cut as much as we can," said Father.

The cut grass was piled in the wagons. It was fun to jump and play on the grass until we started getting bit by bugs. We cried to Mother and she used her medicine salves but the bites itched for days.

"Forty miles, that's a three day drive with healthy animals an' ours are plumb tuckered," said Uncle. He hunkered down on his heels in the shade of our wagon, scratching his leg. "Damnation! Tamsen, you got some more of that salve? My legs're on fire."

"I think we got enough hay," said Father, "but some don't have much to carry water in."

"A critter needin' two gallons a day, we cain't carry near enough."

"We ain't got no choice, Jake."

Before us lay a broad salt plain where grew only thorny, stunted bushes. Our direction took us toward a mountain and after a time we began to ascend, nooning by the side of a spring high up on the mountain. After a rest we journeyed on, descending to the foothills of this mountain to a place where the road began a climb over very steep hills. After much effort we crossed and camped on a ridge on the western side. Ahead was the salt flats, stretching farther than we could see.

In the morning we began the desert drive. At times the wheels of the wagons would sink into soft sand and mud, at other times the hooves of the oxen would break through a hard crust which cut and bruised their feet. The wagons were strung out with ours in the rear.

The desert was a blinding glare, like snowfields in bright sun. A suffocating dust hung above the wagons, caking the nostrils of animals and men, blistering our skin, burning our eyes. The livestock snorted and sneezed, trying to get the dust out of their nostrils.

We saw mirages. Some thought they saw people coming, that Hastings was coming back to help us, but it was our own images reflecting back at us. We saw lakes, beautiful cool blue lakes shimmering in the distance. Then the lakes would disappear and in their place would be more glaring hot salt flats.

On the morning of the third day, several of the group reached a spring at the base of a mountain known as Pilot Peak. We were still well behind and the Reed wagons were yet behind us.

Then disaster struck the Reed family. Mr. Reed had ridden forward in search of water and was returning to his wagons to help his oxen when he met his teamsters driving his unyoked oxen ahead. Pointing to the high mountain on the horizon he told them there was a spring at the base of the mountain. He instructed them to bring the oxen back after they were refreshed and he continued on to his wagons.

All the next day the Reed family waited in the desert heat expecting their teamsters to return, but there was no sight of them. They used the last of their water. That night they huddled together with their dogs, shivering in the cold. In the morning they began to walk. The children cried for water. Mrs. Reed gave them each a piece of lump sugar to suck on, hoping to bring a little moisture to their parched tongues. Late that night they caught up with Uncle Jacob's family, already asleep.

In the morning Aunt Betsey fed them a breakfast of bread and gravy, and when Jacob returned with his refreshed animals he took his family and the Reed family to the spring. They discovered that the Reed oxen had gotten away from the teamsters and stampeded off into the desert.

The dry drive wasn't forty miles, but seventy-five or more. The company lost thirty-six oxen on the journey over the desert, and almost half belonged to Mr. Reed. The company remained at the spring a week searching for the missing livestock, but none were found.

"James is gonna have to leave two of his wagons, an' we don't have enough good animals to pull all three of ours," said Father.

"Which wagon will we leave?" asked Mother.

"The blue wagon's racked to pieces anyways, we'll leave it."

The company took stock and determined that some did not have enough provisions to see them through to California. Mr. Stanton and Mr. McCutcheon volunteered to go ahead to Sutter's Fort for supplies. They would return and meet us on the road.

On we toiled, the tortured shriek of the wheels accompanied by the curses and shouts of the drivers urging the teams forward. Several times we stopped and the men hammered wedges into the wheels to tighten them. The country began to improve and we found good water and grass on the eastern slopes of the valleys.

We crossed still another pass and descended into a fine valley beyond. Two more days westward and then in the hazy distance appeared a high range of mountains running north to south directly in our westward path. We could see no pass, no gap in this range that seemed to run for hundreds of miles.

"From what I learned from Hastings and others," said Mr. Reid, "we should have come to a westward river by now, but it looks like we'll have to cross another range of mountains before we find it. We'll follow that river for a good distance and then it drops into a sink. Then there's a desert to cross."

"Oh God, I thought we were out of the blamed deserts," cried Mrs. Murphy. She stabbed her finger at Mr. Reed. "It's your fault. You talked us into takin' that *Hastings' long trip!* Now you don't even know where the river is." She began sobbing.

"Madam, you, and everyone with you, made the decision for the route."

"You insisted on that route. You said the road would be made. You're a liar."

Mr. Reed's face flushed. Mrs. Reed stepped in front of Mrs. Murphy.

"How dare you call my husband a liar, you Mormon tramp!"

Mrs. Murphy raised her hand as if she intended to hit Mrs. Reed. "You snob! You think you're so high-falutin'—"

Mother stepped between them, pushing them apart. "Please, Levinah, go back to your wagon. It's hot and we're all tired. All of us are sorry we followed Hastings."

Mrs. Murphy's son-in-law, Mr. Foster, pulled her away, still sobbing and shrieking. "Tramp! She called me a tramp."

Mrs. Reed began to whimper and it seemed she might faint. Mr. Reed held her up.

Mother looked at her closely "James, take her to your wagon, I'll bring some medicine."

When Mother returned she told Father what had happened. "She was prostrate and sure that another of her headaches would start. She'll be bedridden for days now."

The next day the wagons stopped and the men convened, looking at the mountain range ahead.

"There's nothing that looks like a pass," said Mr. Reed. "Should I go ahead and scout it out?"

"Hastings would've done that," said Father. "I wonder how far ahead they are."

"They're three weeks ahead at least," Mr. Eddy said disgustedly. "When I get to California I'm goin' to find Hastings an' beat the b'jesus out of him."

"Eddy, you're whistling Dixie. Fellows like that there Hastings always get away with their doin's. It's the honest man that catches hell."

To get around the range of mountains, we were forced to take a long detour, trailing south three days until the road took a turn to the west. We ascended and then descended a gap in the mountains and made camp.

"I followed the road up a piece an' all I can see is the trail headin' north," said Noah.

"It should cut to the west soon," said Mr. Reed.

It didn't. Not for three more days. We were only a mountain range away from where we had camped six days before to the east. After two days more of travel, we found the Humboldt River. It was a pitiful excuse for a river—shallow, with warm unpleasant tasting water, but with good grass in its meadows.

"From what we was told, it's nigh on to two hundred miles to where this river goes into a sink," said Father.

"That's two or three weeks of travel. How much farther, do you reckon, to the mountains of California?" asked Mr. Pike.

"Must be four hundred miles yet, likely it's thirty more days of travel. It's the last of September. I think we're still all right. I'd be more comfortable if we had more provisions, but Stanton an' McCutcheon should be gettin' back soon."

Our animals were in better shape than most of the others and our family group drew ahead by a day or two. We encountered a long, steep sandy hill and had no great difficulty in surmounting it, but when the group behind began to ascend this hill an altercation broke out between Mr. Reed and John Snyder, who was driving one of the Graves' wagons. It was hot and arduous, and tempers were short.

The Reed wagon, driven by Milt Elliot, was trying to pass the Graves wagon and became entangled with it. Mr. Snyder became very angry, thrashing at his oxen to get them to move faster. Mr. Reed came up and the men got into it. The argument became very heated, and John Snyder began hitting Mr. Reed with the butt-end of his whip. Mrs. Reed became frantic, rushed between them and was struck by the heavy whip handle. Fearing for his wife's safety, Mr. Reed drew his knife and plunged it into Snyder. The wound was mortal.

Mr. Snyder was wrapped in a shroud with a board below and a board above, and a funeral service was conducted. When the grave had been filled in, angry sentiments against Mr. Reed flew about the camp.

A decision was made to banish Mr. Reed from the company. When Mr. Reed reached our camp, Mother treated the wounds on his scalp.

"The man hit me several times with his whip handle. Margaret was so distraught she could not get up from her bed. Virginia and Milt will look out for her the best they can, but I am very concerned for my family. I dislike to leave them with those people. They promised they would look after them, but I have no confidence that they will do so with much charity."

We heard more of this story when the group again came together. The Graves family was very angry.

"It warn't no self defense. It was murder pure and simple," said Mr. Graves. "If'n it was up to us we'd have hung him right there."

Virginia was adamant that her father had done nothing wrong and was furious at what the company had done.

"My father was sent out into an unknown country without provisions or arms and even his horse was at first denied him. He went, *not* because of what they did but to bring back supplies to help the company—this miserable, ungrateful company!"

"Mr. Herron went with him, he wasn't alone. I'm sure he'll be all right," Father told the family.

We plodded on, rounding the big bend of the river. We were strung out along the route in separate knots of wagons, with no cohesion, no unity. The alkali soil rose in clouds of dust, settling on everything, caking on our hair, our bodies, our clothing. The sun was tormenting during the day, the cold tormenting at night. While out hunting, two men were shot at by Indians.

"The Indians ran off Graves' horses night before last, now last night they ran off eighteen head of cattle. We got to make a better job of watching the stock," complained Father.

The groups came together again, and we made our way along the river, losing more cattle from exhaustion and bad water. Then the Indians added twenty-one livestock to their tally in one night. Finally we reached the area where the river disappeared into a sink and faced another dry desert.

Crossing over a low ridge of sand hills, we came into heaps of dry and ashy earth, the oxen sinking in many places to their bellies. We made a dry camp, our animals exhausted from the work and the lack of food and water. Fear for the future began its torture.

Oct 9

We've had to lighten our wagons again. It breaks my heart to leave my box of books & the school supplies, but I realize the necessity. George put off my rocking chair, but I refused to allow it. I have been cheered by its presence for so long. It belonged to my dear mother & all my babies have been rocked in that chair. It is my touchstone, my reminder of all most dear.

We plodded on, ascended a ridge, and stopped on the crest to survey the valley in front of us. We saw no green to signal a source of water, only dry, shimmering hot desert. Now our family group and the Murphy family group were in the lead, the rest falling behind.

In the group behind us, Mr. Hardcoop failed and for the third time could not stay on his feet. Mr. Keseberg, with whom he had been traveling, put him out of his wagon to save his animals. Mr. Hardcoop then asked Mr. Eddy to allow him to ride in his wagon, but he put him off also, saying that perhaps later, after getting through the deep sand, he could allow him to ride. All the people were walking to save the strength of the animals.

That evening, Mr. Hardcoop did not come up. Some wanted to go back to find him but the use of a horse was not given. Mr. Hardcoop was abandoned.

We camped near hundreds of springs that seethed with steam and bitter boiling water. A rumbling noise came from under the ground.

"Girls, do not get near any of the holes. This must be where Mr.

Clyman lost his dog when it jumped into one of the boiling springs. We must tie up the dog or show him the danger," said Mother.

"When I said there was plenty of hell on earth I didn't know of this place, but it sure qualifies," said Father.

"These boilin' springs might be good for washin' clothes," said Aunt Betsey. "One a' those holes threw up a shirt or some such cloth. Looks like somebody threw their clothes in, thinkin' the next spout would spit 'em out all cleaned up, but it didn't happen fast enough."

The company moved on, strung out in groups along the road. Only one ox was left to Mr. Wolfinger and one to Mr. Eddy. Mr. Eddy had to abandon his wagon and gear. Now he and his wife were forced to carry their two little children across a burning desert. They set out with nothing but the clothes on their backs and a little lump sugar to eat. Mr. Eddy, desperate to provide water for his children, begged Mr. Breen for water and was refused. Mr. Eddy told Father later that he took the water at gunpoint.

With the abandonment of the Eddy wagon, the situation of Mrs. Reed and the children also became desperate, as for nearly a month they had been traveling with the Eddys. From all the plenty with which they had started, now they were reduced to a few changes of clothing and some blankets.

Mr. Wolfinger decided to make a cache and Mr. Spitzer and Mr. Reinhardt offered to stay behind to help him. Mrs. Wolfinger went on, walking with some of the women.

As a point of a mountain was rounded, we saw in the distance, glimmering behind a line of trees, the Truckee River. Crazed with thirst, the animals set off toward the river at a pace we didn't know they could achieve in their weakened condition. The wagons bumped and lurched behind them as they went pell-mell down the riverbank.

In the evening Reinhardt and Spitzer came in and told that Mr. Wolfinger had been killed by Indians. Three men went back to look for him, found the wagon and oxen, and brought it in. Everyone gathered around Mrs. Wolfinger.

"We found the oxen grazing along the river unyoked an' the wagon sittin' there," reported William Graves, "but nary a sign of Mr. Wolfinger an' no sign of Injuns either, Mr. Donner."

Mrs. Wolfinger was agitated. *"Das Geld! Es ist kein hier. Haben Sie seinen Geld Beutel grefunden?"*

"Mr. Rinehardt, what is she sayin'?"

"I tell her that her husband wass kill by Indians and nossing can be done. She grieves that he won't haf a proper burial."

"Tell her we can't go back to find his body, that we're very sorry for her loss," said Father.

Mother tried to console Mrs. Wolfinger, but she kept crying and trying to tell us something that could not be understood. Father shook his head and made a gesture of helplessness. *"kein geld*—I think she's saying their money is gone."

"I asked Mrs. Keseberg to talk to her," said Mother. "She refused and Mr. Keseberg refused also. After all I did to help them. It makes me so angry."

"When we get to California we'll bring it up to the authorities there. What more can we do now?"

"We could have a tribunal of some kind."

"Tamsen, we've only suspicions, no proof. An' those German boys are stickin' together tight an' won't take it kindly were we to accuse them."

"The men obviously lied," said Mother. "They said the Indians killed Mr. Wolfinger and burned the wagon. The wagon and oxen are found unharmed. Indians would not leave oxen, they've been following us for weeks to get our animals."

"Well, I don't see that anythin' can be done. I'd like to get shut of all the problems these people have. It's blamed hard enough to look after our own."

Chapter Eight

We reached the mountains of California,

but more tragedy awaited us.

We were into October with still a long way to go. The valley of the river became narrow and walled in on both sides by high ranges of barren mountains. We wound our way through the canyon, crossing again and again as the river lapped against one steep side and then the other. In places there was no level ground and we were forced to the hillsides.

As the sun rose in the sky, warmth would chase away the chill, but as it finished its arc and fell in flames among the hills, the cold would again fall upon us. We saw numerous tracks of animals and also tracks of Indians. We caught glimpses to the west of high mountain peaks covered with snow. The Breen and Murphy wagons took the lead and we lost sight of them. After crossing many, many times, the trail left the river, winding up a canyon to the south.

"Why is the road leavin' the river? Don't make sense. We been told this river flows into a big valley that's just before the California mountains."

Father called to Noah. "Go on up the river. See if there's a road. I'm gonna ride up this canyon to see what it looks like."

Noah returned first. "I seen why the trail had taken off up the canyon. Up ahead the river narrows down an' goes between some cliff-like places. Where it opens up it's right soft an' marshy. The big valley's past that. I don't think we can get our wagons through there. I hope that canyon's goin' to be easy like. George ain't back yet?"

"I see him coming yonder now."

Father dismounted and Jim took his horse.

"Well, there's a road, but it's a steady uphill climb for three, four miles. The worst part is that after you get up to the top, there's a sharp decline. Noah, does it look like we can follow the river?"

"It don't look likely, Mr. Donner. I think we'll have to take this here canyon."

All walked to save the oxen. The wagons creaked and groaned and the oxen murmured as they were goaded on. The wind came up, slicing us with its cold sharp edges. As the wagons moved upward, we found Uncle Jacob sitting by the side of the road.

Mother looked closely at him. "Something is wrong, Jacob. You look very sick."

"I just cain't get my breath. All'a sudden I just got weak an' liked to pass out. My palpitator is banging against my ribs, seems like."

"Let's take a rest," said Father. "I'm tuckered out myself."

After our meal we continued on. As we attained the top of the ridge, we looked down a very steep grade into a narrow canyon.

"It's past perpendicular, George," said Uncle.

"I reckon we're gonna have to lower 'em down with ropes. Look off yonder, you can see the valley."

"And yonder still, that must be the mountains of California. We're almost there."

"It's a mighty imposin' sight."

With ropes around a big tree, the wagons were eased down the steep slope. At the bottom the teams were yoked up and we started again through a narrow canyon, in one place so tight between high rocks that our wagon hubs scraped on each side.

It was late afternoon when we emerged from the canyon, moving down a wide gentle slope. Ahead marched a range of high mountains towering over a wide valley ringed with brown hills. As the sun sank behind the high mountains, color flamed across the tops of the hills.

"Oh, such a pretty scene, and what beautiful colors! I should like to paint this," exclaimed Mother.

Uncle Jacob pointed. "See there to the north, those white tops? It's the rest of the company."

"Let's make camp. We can't catch up with them today, it'll take a day to get across the valley."

Dawn came blustery and cold. We moved across the valley, fording several creeks, our wheels crunching through ice that coated the shallow ponds. The wind whipped against us, flapping and snapping the wagon covers. The valley floor was a sagebrush plain, crossed with a few flat streams and sloughs fringed by willows. As we moved to the north side of the valley, we saw herds of deer and antelope.

In mid-afternoon we came up to the rest of the company. Milt Elliot came to us soon after we situated our wagons and put the oxen to graze.

"Looks like you haven't lost any more stock. Have you had any more trouble with the savages?"

"No, but they're out there watchin' for a chance," said Father.

Milt took off his hat and twisted it in his hands. "Things ain't good between Miz Reed an' the others an' they don't have any food to speak of. Could I bring her an' the children to stay in your camp?"

"Of course," Mother told him.

"What came of her supplies?" asked Father.

"They divided their provisions between several others back in the desert when we had to leave the last wagon. I think most of it's been used up."

"Well, Reed should be comin' back soon an' the other men too. They'll have supplies. They should have been back by now."

The Indians shot arrows into the animals at night, killing them or wounding them so badly that they couldn't go on. Then we were struck by more tragedy. Mrs. Murphy's son-in-law, Mr. Pike, was killed. The details were given us by John Denton who'd been in the camp at the time of the accident.

"The blokes were talking of going ahead to get supplies and were sitting around making plans. They noticed the fire was getting low and one chap handed the gun to the other as he got up to get a piece of wood. It went off into his chest."

Mr. Pike died and his body was wrapped in a blanket and buried in a shallow grave.

"I can't help but think of how our company now cares for our dead," Mother said sadly. "Early in the journey Mrs. Keyes was laid to rest in a wood coffin with full funeral rites and a carved memorial. Mr. Halloran was given full Masonic rites and a coffin. Now Mr. Pike, this morning full of life and vigor, is dead, and laid to rest in a grave with only a blanket wrapped around him. No doubt in a few days an Indian will be parading the blanket in front of his miserable brush hut."

"Them pepperbox guns is risky," said Uncle Jacob.

"Seems like we've had more than our share of troubles," said Father. "We need to lay by here and let our animals recruit."

"Yeah, but you see the snow on top of that mountain yonder? We cain't be stayin' here long, or we might not get over at all."

"It's the end of October. It's way too early for the passes to fill with snow. We'll have time to recruit here, but I worry about havin' enough provisions. Sure wish those fellows would get back with supplies."

With so few men to stand guard, the cattle were easy pickings for the Indians. One morning a Paiute man crept up and began shooting arrows into the cattle. Mr. Eddy, enraged, aimed and fired, and the Indian toppled down a slope into dense bushes.

"I don't feel good about Eddy killing that Indian," said Father later. "It will only inflame them to more hostility. But the other side is that maybe they'll stay off from us."

"We're weak and they know it," said Uncle. "I see 'em standing off, making their gestures at us. They don't want us to leave 'til they gets 'em all."

The Breen family group left the next morning to begin the ascent of the mountains. We were anxious to continue, but Father felt that our oxen were still too poor to pull the wagons.

Oct 24

Our oxen recover slowly, and ourselves also. Our wagons are in deplorable condition. We're busy repacking and allocating the goods between the two wagons to even the weight. The men have been making repairs as best they can. George thinks it is perhaps two weeks to the settlements, and our journey will be over. A presentiment of something ... I can't tell what it is ... is scaring me. I feel compelled to gather whatever wild food I can find. Today we found junipers growing on a hillside nearby our camp and I took berries, roots and bark. In the afternoon I dug cattail roots, ending with about two bushels of the cleaned and trimmed roots. The girls found enough berries to make two pies, which was only a small piece for each when divided, but was appreciated much.

The following morning the Murphy family chained up and moved out. The German men stayed with us, as they had their gear in Mrs. Wolfinger's wagon.

That evening we hunched around the fire wrapped in blankets for our evening meal. The dry leaves in the cottonwood and aspen trees rustled and shook in the wind that rose and fell like swells on a body of water. The canvas on the wagons and tents snapped and whumped, straining against the poles and tethers.

One of our horses lifted his ears and knickered, his haunches twitching nervously. Father stood up and picked up his rifle. Off in the distance we heard a faint clattering sound, a sound of hooves moving over rocks and then a voice broke the stillness.

"Halloo, the camp."

"It's men a'comin', an' horses."

We rushed to the opening between the wagons. Shapes appeared out of the dusk. It was Mr. Stanton and two of Mr. Sutter's Indians. They were mounted on mules and leading several others that were heavily laden. Steam rose off the backs of the mules and they snorted and blew, slumping wearily under their packs.

The men dismounted and everyone gathered around them, excited and happy, because now there would be food to get the company to California.

Mrs. Reed made her way to the front of the group and was disappointed to find it wasn't Mr. Reed. "Mr. Stanton, have you any word of my husband? He was going to Sutter's to obtain supplies."

"Yes, ma'am. We met him four days back. He and Herron were in a poorly state, but they're all right."

"Oh, thank God! Children, did you hear? Papa's all right. He got through."

"They got fresh horses and went on to Sutter's for supplies," said Mr. Stanton. "They should be coming on, but it'll take them some time to get situated."

"We're sure glad to see you, Stanton. Why didn't Mr. McCutcheon come back with you?"

"He took sick. I didn't want to wait for him to recover and delay getting back." He turned to Father. "I met three groups of the others ahead of you. Is there anyone behind you?"

"No, Stanton, we're the last."

"Mr. Stanton," said Mother, "we've got coffee here. Please help yourself. I'll fix some food for you and your men."

Mr. Stanton signaled his companions to take the coffee and sat down by the fire. The Indians squatted down.

"Say, George, what's the story about Reed?" asked Mr. Stanton.

"He told us it was a matter of defendin' himself. James did have some bad head wounds from Snyder's whip handle. It's a troublin' thing. But you remember how it was 'fore you left? We were all kind'a crazed after fightin' our way through those terrible canyons an' crossin' the salt flats. If Reed can come back with supplies an' animals, it might help cool down some of the company who're still sore."

Father told Mr. Stanton about Mr. Hardcoop and Mr. Wolfinger and the accidental death of Mr. Pike.

"Well, it's over now. In a few days all will be behind us. What do you plan to do in California, George?"

"I'm gonna scout around, find some good horse land. I hope to get a good-sized piece. I hear they measure their holdin's in miles 'stead of acres. What'd the country look like there where you were?"

"It's good-looking country. There's timbered slopes up to these here high mountains. Down farther are gentle hills, good livestock country. I was told it's not good for farming, it doesn't rain in the summer."

"That so?" said Jacob. "We heard there're orchards, vineyards, an' crops growin' almost wild."

"They say that close to a river or stream you can grow most anything with irrigation," replied Stanton. "I was told that over west of the valley of the Sacramento there's a range of mountains and on the other side there's beautiful land. That's where there's orchards and vineyards. Missions were built there years ago and they tamed a lot of the Indians, made them kind of slaves. Then the mission people pulled out or were called back to Spain or somewhere. That's where the Pueblo of San Jose is located. Then there's Yerba Buena, big bay there, connects to the Pacific, I heard."

"*Yerba Buena*, it mean "good plant, good herb," said Juan Baptiste.

"These Indians with me are Sutter's *vaqueros*, work with the cattle," said Stanton. "The *vaqueros* have amazing ability with the rope."

Baptiste went over to the Indians. *"Hablan Español?"* They nodded their heads and Baptiste sat down with them.

"Mr. Sutter's a true gentleman," continued Mr. Stanton. "He lives like a king in a fiefdom, very civilized. I've heard his holdings are impressive. The fort's not much to look at. The buildings are made of mud."

"Reed talked favorably of the Pueblo of San Jose," said Father. "Mrs. Reed's brother Caden wrote him of it. What's goin' on with the Mexican government?"

"Mr. Sutter's fort was taken over by Federal forces. It looks like the country's going to be United States territory. You know, the Mexicans have no mind for business, but with all the Americans coming in there'll be money to be made."

"Stanton, what kind of Injuns be those boys with you?" asked Uncle Jacob.

"These men are Miwoks. The bigger one's Luis, the other is Salvador. They seem to be stalwart and loyal. I couldn't have come back without these men to guide me and work the mules. Mr. Sutter is most generous."

Father shifted around on the stump he was using for a seat, trying to get comfortable.

"Charles, tell us a little about the country we're facin'. What's that pass like?"

"Actually, there's two passes, one at the end of a good-sized lake. The trail goes around the north side of that lake. There's another road to the south, opened by some of the last parties that went over. I suspect that with so many wagons trying to get over at one time, they had kind of a jam-up. The north pass has real steep rock face and the wagons have to be lifted in a couple of places. That takes time. The south way of going is higher, but has a lesser slope."

"Which do you cotton to?"

"The south, since you don't have a lot of men to do that work."

"We're all about half a man. We're pretty much tuckered out."

"It's going to take you three days, most likely, to get to that lake, an' two days to get to the top of the pass. After you get over the pass, it's still hard going, there's many ridges and canyons before you find the foothills and ease of travel."

"Our animals ain't goin' to make it unless we let 'em recruit. They're in bad shape," said Father.

Mr. Stanton nodded his head. "It's prudent to rest your animals here. Mr. Sutter assured me there's very little likelihood that the pass would close this early."

In the morning Mr. Stanton prepared to leave.

"Donner, we can travel much faster with the mules than you can with your wagons. We're goin' on to catch up with the others. We'll take Mrs. Reed and the children."

Father shook Mr. Stanton's hand. "I can't thank you enough for everythin' you've done, Stanton. Once our animals are strong enough, we'll come on."

Mother went to help Mrs. Reed bundle up the things she would be taking with her. "We still have goods in the Graves wagon," she told Mother. "They've promised to take them on to Sutter's Fort. Mr. Reed will be meeting us on the trail with supplies and he'll be bringing horses for us."

Mrs. Reed and Tommy were placed on one mule, Patty and James each behind one of the Indians and Virginia with Mr. Stanton. We watched them make their way to the river and turn west. A moist wind whipped us and we looked up. Dark clouds hid the high spine of the mountain range and misty veils were flowing down the clefts into the canyons.

Mother gathered her shawl tightly around her shoulders. "It makes me nervous to think we're the last people on this trail."

We stayed in camp two days after Stanton and the Reed family left the camp. We faced west and began the ascent. Everyone walked to save the oxen. A light mist began as the men urged the poor creatures to move forward.

The ground was covered with coarse and sharp-edged gravel that cut and bruised the feet of the animals, adding greatly to their distress. To our left rose tall mountains, to our right across the river was a flat-topped hill. Ahead of us loomed the canyon of the river. It was a magnificent sight—the tumbling and sparkling water, the towering mountains with mists hanging on the slopes like thick white spider webs.

We crossed and re-crossed the river, the wagons lurching through gullies and side-slipping across slopes. The river rushed past us, cascading over rough areas and splitting around great boulders as the sides of the canyon began to narrow. The sky became gray and threatening and mid-morning it began to rain. We crossed the river for the last time about eight miles after leaving the meadow and climbed out of the river canyon.

"George, was you counting? How many times in all did we cross that one river?"

"Jake, it was too blamed many."

The next morning we followed a stream on an easy incline toward the mouth of a narrow, winding canyon. The forest began here and we enjoyed the clean smell of the pine trees, so agreeable after breathing desert sand and alkali dust for weeks.

After entering the canyon the trail immediately went up a steep slope and we were above the canyon. As we stopped to rest we looked to the east from whence we had come and could see, far below, the valley we had left the morning before.

"That there valley would be a good place to settle," said Father. "It's good horse and cattle country."

"Oh, no. No pioneering in a wilderness for me," said Mother. "I was promised the land of milk and honey and some semblance of civilization. There's nothing here."

"It won't always be that, Tamsen. In a few years there'll be people who'll come and settle. Always have, always will."

We climbed through a thick forest, sometimes in a ravine, sometimes on the ridges above the canyon, only to jolt back down to avoid deep crevices and rocks. Father stopped often to let our animals rest. In the afternoon the clouds disappeared but the wind picked up. It was late in the day when we reached the summit.

"George," said Uncle Jacob, "we can't camp here. There's no water an' grass, but down below there's a meadow."

We looked down into a valley surrounded by high mountains. We could see that the road down the steep slope was grooved from the locked wheels of wagons.

"Let's go on down now," said Jacob. "The stock'll be able to graze all night. That mountain we came up has plumb wore them down."

"All right. It'll be dark soon, we've got to move fast."

There was a lot of confusion, the women and children gathering up to walk down, the men unhitching oxen. Uncle Jacob yelled at William to start the horses down. Georgia and I had crawled inside the wagon, exhausted. Mother asked Father if we shouldn't walk down. We begged to stay in the wagon.

"Well, it's goin' to be hard for them to walk down, it's so steep an' slippery. I think they'll be better off in the wagon."

"I want to take them out."

"Tamsen, don't fuss. They'll be fine."

As our wagon was being eased over the edge of the decline, Mother started down with the other girls. The wagon creaked and groaned as it took the strain from being lowered. We slid to the front of the wagon, grabbing for something to hold on to. We heard a loud crack and the wagon sprang forward. Then a terrific jolt as the wagon thumped over on its side, shuddering to a stop at the bottom of the slope. Georgia was found quickly, but it took a while before Father and Uncle could find me under all the things. Mother said that I was knocked unconscious.

We were quite shaken, but not hurt.

"I shouldn't have left the girls in the wagon. You were right, Tamsen. I'm a damned fool."

"They're all right, George. Don't fret."

"The axle's busted through, Mr. Donner," called one of the teamsters.

"Nothin' we can do about it tonight. Let's get the last wagon down. We'll have to make camp here."

Uncle Jacob pleaded with Father to leave the wagon. "It's goin' to take us a day to make a new axle."

"Jacob, I ain't going to leave this wagon."

"If'n we don't get over the pass the goods're not goin' to mean anythin' no ways, George."

"One day ain't gonna make a difference."

Mother pointed to the sky. A huge full moon was rising over the tree tops on the mountain.

"I don't like the looks of that ring around it," said Father. "Back home that would mean a storm comin'."

The next morning the men felled a tree to fashion another axle. It took all day to do the rough shaping. As they were working the chisel slipped, cutting a deep gash in Father's hand. Mother cleaned the wound and bound his hand up in cloth strips.

"Don't fuss, Mother. It's nothing to worry about. We're almost finished with this shapin', but it's nigh to dark. We'll have to finish tomorrow."

The next morning Mr. Reinhardt and Mr. Burger came over to Father.

"We're going to go on. We catch up with the others," said Burger.

"Frau Wolvinger, her wagon haf our gear, she vill go with us," said Mr. Reinhardt.

Father put down the tool he was holding. "I can speak a little German, but not enough to carry on a conversation. I want to know if she's in agreement with you men carrying her off."

"*Nein!*" she said. Even I knew what that meant.

"Well, it seems Mrs. Wolfinger wants to remain with us. If you want to set out walkin', she'll carry your gear on for you."

"Ve cannot carry what ve need," said Mr. Reinhardt angrily. "That iss the same to tell us ve cannot go."

"I ain't tellin' you one way or t'other. I need to get back to the work."

The two men turned away, but they didn't make any move to leave the camp.

"George," said Mother, "I think it would be a good idea to keep our horses close."

Father looked at Mother for a moment, then called Solomon to him. "Solomon, bring the horses up to camp an' stay with them."

"What for? Hey, Uncle George, there's two riders comin'." Solomon pointed.

"I see them. Do what I told you."

It was Mr. Stanton and one of the Indians.

"Hey, George, Jacob. It looks like we aren't going to make it over. The top is snowed in with ten or twelve feet of snow. The others are building cabins to keep out of the weather until we can make another try. They're about twenty miles ahead at the bottom of the pass."

"Where's the other Indian?"

"There's deer up there on that ridge. I heard a rifle shot as we were coming down so he'll be coming along shortly. Maybe your women folk will cook some of the meat for supper."

That evening Mr. Stanton told us of all that had happened to the rest of the company. "We tried to get over several times, different groups of us. The last time we tried, we packed some goods on oxen and mules and started out on foot, but no sooner did we get on the road than it commenced to storm again and we had to go back. A cabin's there that was built by a party that old Greenwood led out in '44. Breen took that, and Keseberg's building a lean-to on it. The Murphy woman's bunch is building a cabin. The Graves family's working on a double cabin, Mrs. Reed and some others to be in the other side. It's going to be crowded. The two fellows and I will have to make something for ourselves."

The next morning Mr. Stanton and the Indians prepared to leave. "George, we're going on back, we need to commence on making some shelter."

On we toiled, over low hills and through rolling, heavily timbered country. We walked close by the wagons, trying to lessen the pelting of rain and sleet and the cutting wind. We stopped in late afternoon. Father put the wagons close together and stretched a canvas overhead. We ate our supper and listened to the rain and sleet beat upon the canvas. We were glad to be out of the weather next to a roaring fire.

"Folks, tomorrow will be a better day. It's early to have such deep snow," said Father. "It'll likely melt. We'll just have to wait it out."

"Yes, surely it won't keep on," said Mother.

It was a bitter disappointment, knowing we were trapped in the mountains, at least for the time being.

The next day a piercing wind again lashed at us with brutal cold. Ice

particles rattled off the canvas covers of the wagons and our frozen clothing. It began snowing heavily and became hard for the oxen to pull the wagons.

"The oxen're wore out," said Father. "I don't think we can make it to where the other people are camped. Noah, take the mare and ride ahead, scout out a good camp."

Sleet, snow and wind battered us as we pushed on, barely making out the trail, a white depression in an expanse of snow-topped sagebrush. It was almost dark when we found Noah coming back.

"There's a place ahead 'bout three miles," he shouted against the wind, pointing off across the plain. "It's off the road a piece, but there's no place close to the road that offers wood or grass."

There was only a sage-covered plain with nothing to slow down the bitter winter wind.

Chapter Nine

The snow became too deep for our oxen to continue,
and we hastily built crude shelters.

The site was a good one—a clear flowing stream, a meadow covered with grass and an abundant supply of dead-fall wood. The men commenced to cut down trees to construct a cabin when darkness stopped the work. As we went to bed, we saw that the sky had cleared and we could see a panorama of stars twinkling against the black night, but the next morning we found snow covering everything and still coming down.

"The snow's broke in the bows on one of our wagons," said Father. "If'n we don't get it cleared off, it'll break in the others. We've got to get some shelter made to keep us out of the weather 'til we can build somethin' better. I'll set up our tent and make a lean-to around it, against one of them big trees there."

Mother pointed to a huge tree that was twisted and gnarled from the wind. "Let's use that one. It's a grandfather tree and seems friendly to me."

For our shelter, poles were leaned against the tree, similar to an

Indian lodge, only not a full circle. The doorway, on one flat side of the circle, faced southeast, so it would catch sun in the morning. On the other side we placed our tent, the opening facing into the main room. The frame of the hut was covered with limbs and branches, and over that was stretched an assortment of quilts, ground covers, canvas, and hides. Beds were made by driving posts into the ground, connecting these with poles and weaving a layer of pine boughs on top.

"Girls, gather up pine needles to carpet the floor. It will help keep us out of the mud," said Mother.

A pit for our fire was dug next to the tree so the smoke from the fire would be drafted up and out along the trunk. Mother hung a canvas to provide a necessary place near the door opening. Baptiste stretched a buffalo skin over a frame to make a door.

For the single men a similar shelter was fashioned of poles. Uncle Jacob and Aunt Betsey went across to the other side of the stream and found an open space surrounded by pine trees and willows.

"George, look." Uncle pointed across the stream. "See that big downed tree? I'll back my two tents up to that an' build a roof over 'em. Keep some of the weather off'n the tents an' it'll kind'a shelter the cookin' fire. An' that log over there, you see it fallen over the stream? We kin cross over on that. We'll not be so close we'll step on each other's feelin's."

It had been lightly snowing and raining off and on all day, but as the work was almost finished, huge wet snowflakes began coming down, making a plopping sound that became faster and faster. Soon a curtain of white obscured the other huts from our view. The men hurriedly finished up and secured the animals as best they could.

Our new home was furnished with our camp table and chairs, our trunks, bedding, and the cooking things. Baptiste found some dry bark under a log and got a fire started. The only way he could get it tindered was by rubbing gun powder into a rag and firing into it.

With a fire burning brightly and food cooking, it was kind of cozy.

Mother placed her rocking chair next to the fire and wearily sat down, gathering we three little ones around her.

"It's nice to get out of the cold and wet, isn't it? I've started a stew in the kettle, we'll have a warm meal."

Mrs. Wolfinger had a place with us and that left all the single men to share one small shelter. Baptiste became unhappy with the arrangement. "I stay here. I no like those men, they tell me do the work, get the wood. Antonio, he go to Jacob's. When the snow stops, we make a camp."

We hoped the storm would quickly pass, but our hopes were in vain. The storms raged for a week. The wind buffeted our flimsy huts, rushing in with icy blasts, sending snow through places that weren't well covered. We would awaken to find a dusting of snow covering our blankets. Father and Juan Baptiste would clear off the accumulation of snow and repair the area the wind had opened up.

Each morning we would push aside the covering on our door hoping we would not have to endure the storm yet another day. We would be bitterly disappointed to see wind whipping and bending the trees and snow coming down. As the snow built up, it would melt and drip down on us. It became difficult to move about and impossible to keep dry. One dark, dreary morning we awoke in a more miserable condition than usual.

"Mother," we cried, "we're cold. Our bed is all wet. There's no fire!"

"Yes, I know. We have no more wood to make a fire. Just stay in bed and I will do what I can."

Mother got up and pulled a shawl around her shoulders. She was followed by Father, exclaiming as his stocking feet hit a pile of snow on the pine needle floor. He sat down on our bed, boots in hand.

"Hows my little girls this mornin'?"

"We're freezing. Can we get in your bed?"

"Sure can, but I think it's some wet too. We'll get a fire soon.

Tamsen, would you pull on my boots? I can't do anythin' with my hand like this."

Mother was poking the cold ashes in the firepit, hoping to find a few live coals.

"Baptiste's gone outside already," said Leanna from the bed she shared with Elitha.

"You're pulling the covers off me," moaned Elitha, yanking at the quilts. "It's so damn cold in here. And you little girls stop your whining, you have the dog to help keep you warm!"

Mother frowned. "Ladies do not use that word."

"Ladies who aren't trapped in a miserable cold hut freezing to death and wet to the bone and jammed in with twenty other people in the middle of a miserable cold storm."

I yelled at Elitha. "We don't either have the dog! He went to Baptiste!"

Father frowned at us and that stopped the chatter. "I'll roust the men out to cut wood. I'm worried about the stock. Mother, would you help me with my coat?" Father winced as the rough sleeve scraped against his sore hand. "Can you find something to wrap around my hand? I can't get a glove on."

"Oh, George, your hand looks so bad. I'll treat it as soon as I get some water heated."

Our teeth were chattering, we were so cold. I began to cry, I just couldn't help it. Then Georgia started crying too, and then Frances. Mrs. Wolfinger called to us, motioning us to come to her. We ran across the ice-cold floor, scooting under her covers, which, miracuously, were dry.

Mother tried to cajole us. "Girls, girls, listen, today it's going to stop snowing and the sun will shine. I don't hear the wind this morning, do you?"

We stopped our whimpering and began to chant. "The wind has stopped blowing! The storm king is dead!"

Mother pulled the door open and a riffle of cold fresh air filled the hut. "Oh, I see blue sky! It's stopped snowing!" exclaimed Mother.

"*Señora*. I bring wood. Me you give the shovel."

Mother handed the shovel up to Baptiste and then chunks of wood thudded inside the door.

"Roust the men out and tell them to come here for some breakfast," Father called to Baptiste. He closed the door and began carrying the wood to the firepit. "We need something to tinder the fire."

Mother took the ax and began chipping bark and splinters off the big tree that so stoically spread its arms over our shelter, standing steadfast while the blasts of wind had toppled lesser trees all around.

"I am truly sorry, Grandfather," said Mother, "but I must have some dry kindling. My little girls are cold and hungry. George, we'll have to start the fire with flint. The ashes are dead."

Father knelt before the firepit. "I can't do the flint with only one hand. You'll have to do it."

After several attempts a spark was thrown and a little flame curled amongst the chips and pine needles. Carefully, Mother blew on the flame and soon had a fire going. The men crowded into our hut, hands jammed into their pockets, hunched over from the cold.

"All right, men," said Father, "we've got to find our animals. I wish I could help more, but now my whole arm is festered an' I can't use it."

"I can do nothing unless I get some boots," said Jim Smith. "Mine's come apart with the wet."

"Me, I need boots," said Baptiste.

"You'll have them. We'll have to dig out the back of the wagon to get to them."

Mother filled bowls with mush topped with a dollop of molasses and handed them out to the men.

"When you find the oxen, move them to that patch of willow behind Jacob's tent. If'n they're dead, mark the location."

"How many did we end up with?"

"Twenty when we got here, if I recollect right," replied Father. "An' two horses. The horses would'a put their tails to the wind an' found a clump of trees for shelter."

As the men finished, they put their bowls and cups in the big washtub by the fire. "Thank'ee ma'am, *Danke*, missus," they said, as they left the hut with Father.

"Elitha, Leanna, please, will you get the little ones washed up and changed?" asked Mother. "We must clean up and take the bedding out to dry. I hope we can heat enough water to wash clothes and bathe."

"I want to change too," said Elitha. "I'm sick of these moldy clothes. Get up, you little girls, start moving! The sun is shining today!"

We were happy to get outside, but the bright light hurt our eyes. We squinted and shaded our eyes with our hands. We were astonished at our appearances. The hut was dim and we hadn't realized how pale and sickly looking we had become, but in the bright light, all was starkly revealed.

On all sides the snow was higher than our heads. Baptiste had made a clearing in front of the door and tromped a path through the snow.

"We'll go visit your cousins, but for now I need your help," said Mother. "We must get all our things out to dry and we have to cook food for the men today, they'll be working hard."

In the afternoon the men came back. They were wet, cold, and exhausted.

"Mr. Donner, we didn't find but twelve of them ox, only six alive. There's a couple spots out there where the snow blowed off some. You could see where some of the oxen walked around an' around a tree digging a pit, but there was nothin' for 'em to eat. The six that're alive had gone into the willows an' they weren't snowed under. Looks like they commenced to eatin' willow. We marked the dead ones we found with poles. Those others ain't anywhere near. We've covered the country for a mile around, and no sign of the horses either."

Aunt Betsey had come to our hut to help Mother cook. The bad news set her off into wailing. "Oh, Lord. What're we gonna do now? We have no way to git out'a here. We got no way to pull our wagons. We're all gonna die here an' the sooner the better."

"Betsey, don't talk that way," said Mother. "We can walk, can't we? We walked most of the way here. We can come back for our wagons after we get settled in California. The snow melted a good bit today."

"Betsey," said Uncle Jacob, "stop yore complainin' an' git to cookin'."

"You're a fine one to tell me to stop complaining, Jacob Donner! That's all *you* do. You'd complain if'n you was gonna be hung with a new rope!"

"Men, we need to get one of those dead oxen dressed out." said Father. "If it's clear tomorrow we've got to find the horses an' the rest of the oxen."

"I want a stock of wood beside my door where I can get to it," said Mother.

"Yes," said Father, "Juan Baptiste, you an' Antonio, dig out some of them trees an' drag 'em over here close. We can work on chopping the wood up when we can, we'll have it to hand."

That evening, we all sat around the fire. It was so good to have a fire again. Aunt Betsey hugged her knees and gazed into the fire. "I just get so down. I'm so afraid we won't get out."

"Hush that talk," said Mother. "Yesterday we were wet and cold and had no fire. It was still snowing. Today the sun is shining and we have fire and hot food. So isn't today better than yesterday? Look at the positive side and your worries will recede."

Uncle got up and bent over the fire, tilting the kettle to pour coffee in his cup. "We sure as hell got our tails in a crack now. Should we think about goin' back to that big valley? Likely the snow's not as deep there. We're at a higher elevation here."

"Which valley are you speaking of?"

"The big one where we started up the mountain. Where we stopped an' recruited."

"Well," said Father, "that was maybe thirty, forty miles back. We came over two summits an' they were higher than this here. Am I right?"

Uncle Jacob nodded. "Yeah."

"So, even if it melts off here, it's likely to stay deep on those summits. Mebbe not as deep as on the mountains ahead, but if we go back we can't make a run at the mountain when the weather breaks."

"Ya' know," said Jim Smith, "I'm wonderin' if the oxen an' the horses didn't turn tail an' head back to that deep valley where we camped to fix the wagon. They'd remember all that green grass. They'd have no way a' knowin' it was gonna snow there too. I think I'll make a couple sets of snowshoes tonight an' if someone will go with me tomorrow we'll strike back aways an' see if we can spot 'em."

"If'n they weren't driven off by the Injuns."

"Most likely the Indians would not have been out in the storms," said Father.

"It was 'bout twelve miles, warn't it, Jim? I don't see how you could go that far on snowshoes, it being uphill," said Uncle Jacob.

"We could track back a ways," replied Jim. Father was against this idea. "Jim, if'n it's clear in the morning, go on, but only as far as you can get back by night. If'n a storm comes up again you might be stuck out there."

Jim Smith and Charlie Burger went in search of the missing livestock, returning after dark. "We went back three, four miles an' we found no sign. Not so much as a hair. They've plumb disappeared."

The next day Milt Elliot came with two other men from the other camps. They were preparing to make an attempt to cross the mountains on foot and wanted to obtain goods from Father.

"We're needin' coats, boots, gloves, an' such."

"An' tobacco, " said one of the men.

"Yeah, an' tobacco," said Milt.

"I'll have to pay you in California, Mr. Donner," said Milt. "Mr. Reed didn't leave money with us. Miz Reed couldn't pay cash money for the oxen she bought from Graves an' Breen. They told her she'd have to pay two for one in California."

"How many did she get from them?"

"Four altogether."

That afternoon Milt and Baptiste searched deep into the snow with poles but could not find any oxen.

"Mr. Donner," said Milt, "we're goin' back in the mornin'. Some of your people's wantin' to go too."

"Who all?"

"Uh, John Baptiste, Jim, Charlie, Noah ... an' the Mexican boy. Yeah, I think Antoine's goin'."

"Well, look, Noah, if it looks likely to get over, you an' Baptiste come back an' help us. If'n the ox we still have are still alive, an' the snow stays melted like it is, they can pull the two sleds that Baptiste made. We can load our food an' blankets and such on 'em."

Mother made up a packet of food for them and they set off. Mother and Father talked about our food supplies.

"Should we share our food with the men who have attached themselves to us? They were given a share of the food Mr. Stanton brought and now those provisions are gone. We must think of our own."

"I know, Mother. But we can't stand by and see others starve either."

That night everyone was restless. We knew that things were getting very bad. Mother wrapped herself in a blanket and sat in her chair by the fire, where only a few streaks of red showed under a gray mantle of ash. She poked up the ashes to start some wood burning, moving the tea kettle over the flames.

Elitha got up from bed and sat down in front of the fire. "It's so cold in here, it's hard to sleep."

Flames began flickering around the wood and when the water was hot Mother made tea. I slipped from bed and curled up on Mother's lap. The green wood in the fire popped and sizzled.

"The fire's about the only comfort we have, except for each other," said Mother.

"You have to be right on it to feel it," said Elitha.

"No matter how big the fire is it can't warm the hut," said Mother. "All we can do is bundle up."

A wolf began a crooning howl and soon other wolf voices joined in a chilling chorus.

I shuddered. "I hate wolves, they make me afraid at night. Baptiste says they don't bother people, but I don't believe him."

Elitha began to cry. "I'm sick of being cold and wet and dirty. The hogs back home live better than we do. I'm just so miserable!"

"Do you think you're the only one?"

"No."

"We may be able to leave soon, but if not, we must think of when we can leave. We can't allow ourselves to wallow in despair. Think of things to do to get your mind off the misery. Activity helps."

"I know, I know! But what's the use? We'll probably all die any-way."

"Honey, this will all pass. We'll get to California and have a wonderful life. We just have to grin and bear it for a while."

Elitha wiped her tears with the hem of her night dress and got up. "I started my monthly. Where are the cloths?"

Mother pointed. "Look in the trunk. I burned the old ones, it was so hard to wash them. Wrap some of the cattail cotton inside the cloth, it absorbs well."

Elitha opened the trunk, and took out what she needed. I scooted back to bed.

"Elitha," said Mother, "would you please hand me my tin box? It's there in the trunk."

Mother put more wood on the fire and sat down again, taking her journal and pen and ink from the tin box. She tilted the notebook towards the fire for light as she began to write.

Nov 19

If we don't find the rest of our oxen, our food will only last a month even if we ration it carefully. Wood is hard to obtain. We don't have enough fire to warm us, barely enough to cook our meager fare. Everyone is becoming dispirited. I am also. I must not allow it to show. I confess to you, my journal, fear is gathering. I feel it, but I force it back. I must remain strong for my husband and my children. Surely we'll be able to get out before our food is gone. Oh God, deliver us from this tomb of snow.

The next day was fine and clear. After we'd cleaned and straightened up our quarters, Mother told us we would visit our cousins and take some meat to them. We tramped over a path that Juan Baptiste had cleared to the other hut. After every storm the path grew higher and higher and Baptiste would cut more steps in the snow. We slipped and slid down to the stream and gingerly teetered over the log bridge.

We found Uncle's family crouched up in their beds, the little ones listless and sickly looking. Aunt Betsey pointed to the cold firepit.

"There's so much water dripping down I cain't keep a fire. We're wet all the way through from the snow melt an' cold all the time. Can Baptiste get out an' get us some wood? I cain't even cook. Not that I've got anythin' much to cook."

"Baptiste's not back from the other camps," said Mother. "We've brought some meat for you."

Betsey moved to a chair and sat down dejectedly, her little ones clustering around her.

"Jake in bed?" asked Father.

"Cain't get him to stir at all."

"Let's get a fire started for them," said Father. He looked around the hut. "There's no wood. Elitha, you an' Leanna go fetch some kindlin' an' wood an' bring that ground sheet that's on the wood pile. Bring some coals too."

They returned dragging a skin piled with wood. Father put some large pieces in the wet firepit.

"It's hard to do this with only one hand. Solomon, break up some of that wood an' get that fire goin'." He yelled in the direction of the tent that was used for sleeping. "Jacob, get up. I've only got one good arm and I still do more than you."

Uncle appeared in the tent opening. "George, I'm sick. Cain't do nothin'."

"Well, I'll allow you look sick. Now, Solomon, you and William get out there, we've got to work on your roof. Start clearin' off some of the snow."

"Our shovel done broke, Uncle George. We ain't got nothin' to shovel with."

"You just now worryin' about it? Go get ours. Solomon, start pulling some of them hides off the roof."

We heard a lot of crunching around on the snow, then a pile of snow dropped into the hut and we could see the sky through the roof.

"They's tearing the place apart. It'll be worse than before," said Aunt Betsey. "We might as well just give up an' take some poison."

Father struggled for a while with the work and then threw the materials he was holding in his good hand down. "We've got to have more help."

"Let's have everyone go to our camp," said Mother. "I'll get a meal started."

"Yeah. Elizabeth, take yer kids an' go on with Tamsen. Elitha, you an' Leanna help with the young'uns."

It was late in the day before the men came to supper. As we ate, we could hear the melting snow dropping here and there, making a concert of plopping sounds accompanied by sizzles as drops would hit in the fire. The wind came up, howling and beating at our weak structure, the assortment of hides and covers flapping and flailing about. The flames of the fire whipped and sputtered as freezing drafts swirled around inside. Aunt Betsey stared dejectedly into the fire.

"Our camp is the most miserable, coldest place I've ever been in my life, an' half has done blown away."

"What we got done today will help," said Father. "If it's clear tomorrow we'll get it closed more. The boys need to get you a stock of wood."

"You know," said Mother, "the layers of snow tend to provide shelter that the wind can't get through. Kind of like sod or dirt would. If you have the boys build walls of snow around the hut it will keep some of the wind out. You could cut bricks of snow, big bricks, like the Eskimos do. Have you ever seen a picture of an igloo?"

"I never heard of any of it. Tamsen, the snow's already a wall aroun' the hut," said Uncle.

"Yes, but you need space and a barrier between you and the snow. If the snow is right up against the canvas of the tent, the cold transfers to the inside. If there's a barrier and an open space, it won't allow as much cold through. There'll be more warmth for the same amount of fire."

"Tamsen, I cain't hardly lift my arm, much less a shovel of snow," whined Jacob. His eyes were sunken and circled with dark skin, his cheeks hollow.

"Get those boys to do it. They need to work to stay strong. We'll all need our strength to walk out."

"I'm gettin' out of here," yelled Solomon. "I'm leavin' an' goin' over to the other camps. The first good day I'm goin' over the mountain."

"No, you ain't," said Betsey. "You're stayin' right here. You'll get out there an' get lost, I know you. Noah's comin' back to tell us if we kin get over. Then we'll all go."

Uncle Jacob slouched against a cutoff stump. "I cain't walk half a mile," he said dejectedly, then he looked up and there was a little hope in his voice. "I might be able to go on a mule or horse if'n Reed got back with some."

"Jacob," said Father, "there's no sense to mopin' an' feelin' sorry for yourself."

"Me an' the boys try to get wood, but we just sink down in the snow, cain't even walk. All the dead wood is buried deep. I cain't find strength enough to get out'a bed, an' there ain't nothin' to get out'a bed for."

"I cain't get any of them to do nothin'," said Betsey. "The place stinks worse'n a skunk's nest an' they won't help clean it up. They won't even go outside to piss anymore."

Chapter Ten

We were trapped in flimsy huts,

battered by storm after storm.

It was about the time of Thanksgiving that Jim Smith and John Baptiste came back from the other camps. The rest of the men that had gone stayed at the other camps.

"Some people, they try to get over, us too," reported Baptiste. "But two days an' we come back. The snow is too deep. The *Señor* Breen, he kill all his *animales*, but others they lose their stock, like us."

Jim Smith rose tiredly from his seat. "There ain't no getting over 'less the storms stop an' the snow hardens up. Mebbe it will be possible fer some that're still strong to make it then. I allow that we're gone coons. We ain't gonna make it out'a here."

From that time, the men huddled in their shelter, making little effort to get wood or keep a fire going, even to cook the paltry provisions they had. Only Baptiste and John Denton moved about. Baptiste would take us little ones to the top of the snow, sometimes making an overhead shelter of his old Navajo blanket, sometimes wrapping us up in it. Often, Mother would join us and Father too. Mother said that living without the purifying effect of the sun was not a healthy thing.

When we had a clear sunny day and a supply of wood to heat water, Mother would drag out the washtub and we would wash clothes and bathe. Over time the fire sank deeper and deeper into the snow until a large pit had formed. This gave mother an idea.

"Baptiste, the fire has melted the snow so much I think that with a little more work we can clear it down to the ground. If we remove the snow from here, where it's melted, over to the door, we'll have a good sized clearing. We'd have protection from the wind when we are out here."

Baptiste started the work and soon everyone was helping. When enough snow was cleared to make a circle of about ten feet across, we were exhausted, but pleased by our accomplishment.

Baptiste continued working over the next few days, carving benches on one side and a new set of snow stairs to the top of the snow. He made snow canyons connecting the wagons to our clearing, and made a camp for himself under a wagon.

The clearing became a favorite place for us when it wasn't snowing. The little circle of Mother Earth under our feet was a pleasant respite from the glaring white snow that surrounded and enveloped us, depressing our spirits.

The second week in December Aunt Betsey came to us, crying and wringing her hands. "Jacob's just laying there like he's dead, but he ain't dead. I don't know what to do."

Baptiste was squatting by the fireplace and looked up. "He no want to live. He die when he get his body to give up."

"How would you know?" cried Betsey.

"I know some things, and this I know," said Baptiste.

We all went to their camp. Uncle was lying in bed and was very weak. Father helped him to a chair at the table. Mother tried to get him to drink the tea she'd made, but he would only take a sip. He laid his arms and head on the table.

"It ain't goin' to help."

Betsey shook Jacob's arm and tried to get him to hold his head up. "How do you know it ain't goin' to help? Oh, Jacob, what am I gonna do with you?" She sank down on one of the beds and slumped over with her head in her hands. "He don't want to live, that's all there is to it."

Uncle Jacob rolled his head to the side and looked up. "George, I seen our farm. In the new country."

"What was it like, Jake?"

"There was a big house, like to home in Carolina. There was green fields, all fenced purty like, an' yer horses, George. You 'member that black you had? He was in the field."

Betsey got up and stood behind Jacob, rubbing his back. "He's been talking crazy like. He said he seen his Pa and Ma."

"I did, sure enough. Pa was mad as hell 'cause we left Illinois. He said we're never gonna see California an' we're gonna die in these god-forsaken mountains. George, bury me deep. I cain't stand the thought of the wolves gettin' at me."

"Jake, the snow's gonna stop. Help is on the way from California. Don't give up."

"Let me rest. I'm powerful tired."

Jacob put his head down again on his crossed arms. His voice was weak, muffled.

"We're paying now fer settin' our sights so high. I reckon the Almighty don't like a man to over aim. If'n he does he sics somethin' on him."

"Betsey," said Mother, "it's best to have the children go to our camp. Betsey—"

"What?"

"Send the children over to our camp."

We all trooped back to our hut. It was early the next morning when Mother and Father came back. "He's gone," said Mother. "Toward morning his body gave up his soul."

"We should never have left home. Jake would still be here." Father began to cry, deep sobs racking his body. We had never seen Father cry before. It was like sharp knives through us.

"Baptiste," said Mother, "we need to dig a grave for Jacob. Get the men to help, and the boys should help too."

"Those men in the hut, they all sick. I think they die soon too. They can do nothing. Maybe Denton, he can help."

It was cold and snowy as we walked solemnly to Uncle's final resting place at the foot of the ridge behind our camps.

Father's face was gray and haggard, and his voice weak and raspy as he read from the Bible.

A ray of sun pierced the clouds and we turned our faces to feel and savor the warmth, but in a moment it was gone and snow began falling again. It melted on our faces and made a white frosty crust on our heads and on our clothes.

Aunt Betsey sank to her knees and brushed the snow away from Uncle's face.

"He looks so peaceful. He's happy he don't have to worry no more, but what about me? What'm I goin' to do?" She pulled the blanket over his face and got up. "Cover him up. He's in a better place. I cain't abide to see him like this out here in this terr'ble, sad, lonely place, no box, no stone, no one to visit his grave."

Father put his arms around Aunt Betsey and held her tight.

"We're gonna have to come back. We'll take him up and carry him to California, we'll make a proper place."

Everyone was crying. We hated to leave Uncle there in the snow.

"We're all gonna die here, George, an' it's yer doin's," moaned Aunt Betsey at our fire. "You and your yondering. Jacob wouldn't have come, but you kept a yammering at him."

"Betsey, Jacob wanted to come just as much!" cried Mother. "We're not going to die here! There'll be people coming any day now to help us. Mr. Reed's spreading the word. He won't leave his family up here. Any day now, there'll be help coming."

Dec 8

It's difficult to write these words, my tears are ruining the paper. Jacob died yesterday. There was nothing we could do. He was in poor health when we left Springfield, and the trials of the journey reduced his strength and exhausted his energy. I fear some of the men will also die soon. Seemingly, they have no desire to live.

Several of the men didn't have the will to live. Smith and Shoemaker had taken to their beds, unable, or unwilling, to move about. Reinhardt seldom arose from his seat by the fire.

Mother was exasperated. "Why aren't you men stirring around? The inactivity will weaken you so you can't do anything. This hut is a pigsty. It's unhealthy."

Mr. Reinhardt stared into the fire. "Vat's the use? Ve die here anyway. *Gott* iss punishing us."

"Why would God punish the little innocent children?"

Jim Smith sat up and swung his legs over the side of the bed. His voice was hoarse and he sucked in air after every few words. "God's fickle. He tempts men to be sinful just so's he can roast 'em later for doin' what he gives 'em a weakness for." He tried to stand, but his legs wobbled and he sank back onto the bed.

"It don't make no sense to me," said Mr. Shoemaker. "Mebbe it keeps Him from gettin' bored, lookin' down an' seeing us squirm and suffer."

Baptiste squatted by Jim Smith's bed and looked at him earnestly. "Is *El Diablo* who asks the man to do the sin. If the man he say yes, is his mistake, not the fault of God. What sin you do that you must die?"

"Nothin' that I can think of. I'm God-fearin', but not a church goer."

"Well, then it is not for sure that you die, because *Dios* he say so. Perhaps you want to die, is so?"

"No, but it's useless to fight. It's gonna happen."

"Then I think that nothing can be done for you. It is too bad. *Vaya con Dios.*"

We were at our fire doing lessons a few days later when the door suddenly opened and a blast of cold air and icy snow swirled around us. A dark shape stood in the bright white opening. We gasped and fled behind Mother. Then the door scraped closed.

"It's all right," said Mother. "Good morning, Mr. Reinhardt. Would you have coffee?"

"*Danke.*" He was weak and shaky, using a stick to steady himself. Mother gestured for him to have a seat on the bench that Georgia and I had just left. He looked around the room, his head moving slowly, his mouth slack, as though he was partly in a stupor. Then he eased down and stared dully into the fire. After a few moments he stirred.

"Where iss Donner?"

"He's resting. Do you wish to speak with him?"

"*Nein.* Iss not necessary."

Mother handed him a mug of coffee. For awhile the only sounds were the crackling of the fire and the wind moaning and sighing in the trees.

"Vere iss the lady?"

"Mrs. Wolfinger? She is there."

Mother pointed to the dark corner where Mrs. Wolfinger had gone when the man had entered the hut. Her eyes glinted in the firelight now and again, but she said nothing.

Mr. Reinhardt did not follow Mother's pointing finger with his gaze. He pulled a leather bag from his coat and held it up.

"I vant you give this to the lady."

Mother took the bag and sat back down but said nothing. A piece of wood in the fire snapped and sizzled. Mr. Reinhardt made a deep sighing sound and his body slumped, the coffee falling to the floor. We were fearful that he'd passed on there on our bench, but he roused himself and with the help of the stick he got to his feet. Mumbling something we couldn't make out, he moved to the door and disappeared in the sudden white glare. Mrs. Wolfinger got up and pushed the door closed. She came to Mother and took the leather bag, pouring the coins into her hand. *"Schmutztitel!"* she exclaimed.

Milt Elliott and Noah James came from the other camps the second week in December. They reported that the situation there was becoming desperate. Milt had a very bad cough and both men's eyes were red and swollen from the snow glare.

"Milford, I'm going to fix you men some food and then I will treat your eyes," said Mother.

"I'll appreciate it, ma'am. They're botherin' me terrible."

After the men had eaten, Father passed out tobacco and Mother made coffee and tea. We asked about the other children.

"They's doin' all right, considerin'. Virginia an' Patty told me to tell you hello an' they wanted to know if'n you had any books you could send. They left everythin' of theirs back in the desert. It gets powerful boring with nothin' to do but sit an' stare at the fire. There was some readin' stuff left in the cabin that the Breens took. We done read it all a hundred times. Mr. Graves is making snowshoes an' gettin' ready to try to get over again. There's about twenty that'll go. We'll go too if'n we can get back before they leave."

"How's he makin' the snowshoes?" asked Father.

"He uses ox bows. Cuts the ox bows in half an' weaves strips of hide in-between."

"My snowshoes, they are much better," said Baptiste.

"I like yours, John," said Noah, picking one of the snowshoes up. "How'd you make it?"

"It is the Indian way. The willow, it is strong and limber, it no break," replied Baptiste.

"You use a willow branch—"

"I put it to the fire for a time an' I peel it an' bend to the shape, you see, an' weave the willow back and forth. Like you make a basket, *sabes?*

"Yeah, yours are better, not as heavy."

Milt continued with his story of happenings at the lake camp. "They've recovered most of the dead animals by now, but it's poor meat an' we ain't got any salt. Miz Donner, do you have any you could share?"

"I have a little, Milt."

"I brung a note from Mr. Stanton. He wants to buy some goods. We're to carry them back with us." Milt pulled a paper from his pocket and handed it to Father. "He written a list. Tobacco is one thing."

"We have plenty of tea, coffee and tobacco we can give you," said Father. "Our cattle's buried under the snow or we could give you some meat. We haven't been able to find any of 'em, our two that were alive died some time back, an' we've used up everythin' but the bones and hides. What's the snow level over there?"

"It was six or eight feet," answered Milt. He began to cough. "Seems like it's not … as deep … over here." His coughing grew worse and he took a swallow of coffee, but almost choked on it. Mother prepared a cough remedy and poured it into a medicine cup.

"Try this, Milt, it might help."

Milt looked at the cup, shrugged his shoulders and downed it.

"She makes us take that stuff all the time. It tastes awful!" exclaimed Frances.

"I guess I tasted worse, but I don't remember when," he said. When his coughing subsided, Milt continued. "Eddy killed a good-sized she bear. He pret' near came to an early end 'cause he wounded it, but couldn't reload 'fore it charged him. It chased him around a tree fer a spell 'fore it gave out. Scared the *bejeezus* out of him. That meat helped, but with so many it didn't go that far."

"Juan Baptiste goes out to hunt when he can, but he hasn't seen anythin'," said Father. "With the snow so deep, we just don't have the strength to go far off."

"An' you have Miz Elizabeth and the children to look after too. Those men don't do much?"

"Well, Smith died two days ago. Two of the others look likely to die. That's what Juan Baptiste says, I ain't been over there. Denton's stayin' at Jake's—Elizabeth's—place to help her out. I can't do much with this hand of mine the way it is. It's just taken the life out of me."

"What're you doin' for it?"

"Tamsen pesters me with all the treatments she can think of."

"Smith, he still in his bed." said Juan Baptiste. "The others, they are dead by now, I think so."

"Well, mebbe we should go check on 'em, at least bury Smith," said Milt.

They returned after a time, a hard covering of ice and snow on their clothes. "We buried all three of 'em," said Noah. "I cain't figure how they could up and die. They weren't starvin', were they?"

"No. They just gave up," said Mother. "I think they felt all was hopeless and they had no reason to live. It was a way to escape the misery."

"I tell you they will die. You don't fight to live, you die," said Baptiste. "Unless it is *El Destino*, then you die anyway. I no scared to die, because the soul, it is here forever, but it is good to live, and I have not lived long enough yet."

After supper Mother sat down next to Father. "George, Noah and Milt are leaving as soon as the weather permits. We need to make up a note for the men to carry to Mr. Sutter. What should we ask for?"

Father reflected for a minute. "Well, we've got to have animals to pack out on."

"He sent some fine-looking mules with Stanton," said Milt.

"Yeah," said Noah, "an' they're lost, likely driven off by those damned savages. Mules are best in snow, I suppose. I don't think Sutter'll have oxen, but mebbe he would."

"Oxen are not gonna be any good in the snow," said Father. "Ask for five mules, two horses, an' food."

It was several days before Noah and Milt could go back to the camps at the lake, and John Denton went with them. They carried a note from Father authorizing Milt to be his agent and purchase at the settlements goods for our relief. It was a few days before Christmas, and our spirits were very low.

"Baptiste," said Mother, "in two days, we will celebrate the Lord's birthday and we *must* have a good meal. I want you to go on a hunt."

"I will try. The snow it is soft. I go to my knees even with the snowshoes."

"Baptiste, use my rifle. Denton worked it over before he left. Get that bundle out from under my bed. Yeah, that's it." Father got up and followed Baptiste, watching as he unwrapped the bundle on the table.

"Good thing he oiled it up good," said Father. "Wolfinger, he had one that was better than this." He turned to Mrs. Wolfinger, standing by the fire. "Mrs. Wolfinger. *Gatte. Durchwuhlen?*" Father held his arm out and sighted along it using his finger as if on a trigger.

"*Nein.* Keseberg."

"Keseberg has it? I guess she has no use for it, but it's a valuable gun. Maybe she can get it back."

"*Nein, geld, geld.*" Mrs. Wolfinger pointed to her open palm.

Father shrugged. "She sold it to him."

Baptiste picked up the gun.

"That Hawkens is a good rifle," said Father. "It'll give you distance, but best you practice a little."

"Baptiste, we will pray," said Mother. "We'll ask God to show us mercy and provide us with a Christmas dinner."

"*Mi abuela,* when she has a need that is *especiale,* she go to the church an' she light a candle. Sometimes it work."

"Then we will do the same," said Mother. She rummaged around in a trunk and found half a candle still in its holder. Kneeling down by the fire, she held the candle to an ember. The flame guttered and then held steady.

"Juan Baptiste, what does your grandmother do when she lights the candle?"

"She make the sign of the cross an' she think what she ask for. Sometimes the *padre* she tell him an' he ask *Dios* for it too."

"Baptiste, you do it the way of your grandmother and then I will do it my way."

She put the candle on the table and everyone gathered around. Baptiste knelt in front of the candle, made the sign of the cross, and whispered fervently. The yellow flame reflected in his eyes. After a while he got up and Mother took his place.

"Our Father, God of us all, we ask you to be with Juan Baptiste as he goes out to hunt. Your will be done, Father, but our need is great. Bring an animal to Juan Baptiste so that we may nourish our bodies as we celebrate our Lord's birthday. Amen."

She stood and took Baptiste's hands in hers. "Juan Baptiste, you are a good hunter. Tell yourself that you will not fail. If you are convinced that you will find an animal to kill it will be more likely to happen than if you do not. You must have every advantage if you are to be successful."

Mother smeared some sooty black stuff all around his eyes. "This will help with the glare, Baptiste. Just don't rub it into your eyes."

When he was ready to go, Mother gave him Father's gloves, a hat she'd made from a soft fur, and a little pack of food. We went from the hut, squinting against the glare. It had snowed during the night but now it looked to be a fine day. We followed Baptiste up the steps.

"God will not let us down, Baptiste," said Mother.

"*Espero que tienes razón*. I hope you are right."

We watched until he disappeared in the dunes of snow. Mother went back into the hut and called to everyone to go outside.

"It's a fine day. We must have a stock of wood and it will be good to move about and get some sun."

We went to Aunt Betsey's and Mother rousted out the two older boys.

"It's Baptiste's job to get wood," complained Solomon. He'd been a little deranged ever since he'd insisted on going over to the lake camps one day by himself. He'd wandered in circles, finally making his way back exhausted and frozen.

"Baptiste is hunting. I know it's hard, but wood we must have."

Juan Baptiste was gone all day, coming back after dark, empty-handed. The next morning he went out again. It had begun to rain.

Mother gathered everyone around the fire, determined to have some semblance of our usual holiday. We'd been moaning and crying, remembering the wonderful Christmas times we'd had back home. We thought of the roast duck, heaps of mashed potatoes, pies. Oh, it was agony.

Mrs. Wolfinger went to the door of the hut and pulled it open to look out. "*Achh, schnee, schnee.*"

"Yes, it's snowing again," said Mother. "Elitha, go ask Aunt Betsey to bring everyone here."

We gathered around the fire. Mother gave each one a share of the last little piece of dried deer meat and a square of hide boilings. One of Betsey's little ones began to cry. "I want bread." Then the others began to cry and whimper too. Mother went to a kettle keeping warm at the fire and took out some flat cornbread-looking cakes.

"Here, I have one for each of you."

"What is it?"

"This is from the inner bark of a pine tree. It has life-sustaining properties—it's not bad tasting either."

"Is it bread, Auntie Tamsen?"

"A form of bread. And my other treat is Indian lemonade. You can have it cold as an iced drink or hot as a tea. It tastes good and it's good for you and because today is a special day, I have sweetened it."

"Mother! You always make us drink it without the sweet!" I cried.

"Well, I have only a little left."

"What's it made of?" asked Betsey.

"It's made from sumac leaves. I gathered a basket of the plant when we were on the road."

"*Ja.* Sumac. *Gut,*" said Mrs. Wolfinger.

Mother gave everyone a drink and a piece of the bread. Some found it agreeable, others did not, but we ate all of it anyway.

"Now," Mother said, "we're going to play a game. In our mind, we'll each picture a room in our new home in California and then describe it. After everyone has described their room, we'll decide who has the nicest. Eliza, you can go first."

"Ummm, I want lots of food in my room like yeast bread with butter an' corn an' apples an' a whole bunch of pies."

"Stop it!" yelled Elitha. "Don't remind us! Just tell us what you want your room to be *like*."

Mother gave Elitha a reproachful look and I stuck my tongue out at her. We played our game, having a little fun for the first time in days and days. Father participated too, insisting that a barn would qualify as a beautiful room.

"No, Father. A barn stinks. How can it be beautiful if it stinks?"

"To a farmer a barn never smells bad. Remember the smell of the hay? Doesn't hay smell good?"

"Close your eyes and see if you can remember the smell of hay," Mother suggested.

"Mother, do you mean green hay from the field or old hay like straw?"

"Either one."

"I can remember the hay in the barn smell," said Frances. "I like it. I like to climb in the hay and play. But it's dusty and makes me sneeze."

"It would be so nice to have some of that straw and hay to put here on the floor, wouldn't it?" asked Mother. "But we do have pine needles. Perhaps today we can collect fresh ones to put down."

"Mother," said Father. "Yesterday a spark pret' near started a fire in those dry needles. It was luck it was right under my feet. Keep 'em away from the firepit."

We played our games all afternoon, taking time to bring in some pine boughs. We put the fresh ones on the beds and the old ones down on the floor.

We were worried about Baptiste. We knew he'd be soaked through and frozen. Late in the day we went out, anxiously looking for sight of him. It had started snowing heavily.

"Oh, why did I send him out?" moaned Mother.

"Mother, I think I hear something," said Elitha.

Straining to see in the direction of the sound, we could see a dark form approaching, barely visable in the white gloom of falling snow.

Mother called and waved her shawl. "Baptiste, Baptiste!" As he approached we could make out what the sound was—Baptiste was singing!

"Dans mon chemin j'ai recontre," he saw us and waved. *"Trois cavalieres bien montees—"*

His clothing was covered with ice and he was wet all the way through, shivering and shaking with the cold. He was pulling a furry shape.

"Mother, Baptiste has killed something!"

We helped him drag the animal to the clearing.

"Elitha, get a blanket," said Mother. "Baptiste, get those wet clothes off and come in to the fire. I'll make some coffee."

"I request of *Dios* many times to send an animal close an' he bring to me a bear cub! But his m-m-mama get mad an' me she almost kill."

"Our prayers were answered, Baptiste."

When Baptiste came inside Father clapped him on the back. "Good work, son. My God, you're frozen! Warm up by the fire. Tamsen, you got coffee made?"

Baptiste told us of the struggle to kill the cub. He'd spied the bears, a mother with two cubs, and he wanted to kill the mother bear, but knew it would be hard with one shot. He decided to kill one of the cubs. He was shaking from the cold, but was so excited that he couldn't stop talking.

"The b-b-bears are coming toward me, but I ask myself how I do this without the mother she attack me. I think they will p-p-pass this big tree, so I hide and I wait. I think they never come they are so slow! I am f-f-freezing from the rain an' s-snow. After a time they come. I take the careful aim an' I k-kill the little one."

When Baptiste had warmed himself and put on dry clothes he and Mother began to cut up the bear.

"How did you manage to drag this animal so far?" asked Mother. "This is a second year cub."

"Him I pull with my rope. I no think I can do it, but I no want to cut him in pieces. The wolves they will eat him before I can go back. So I pray for strength, but many times I stop to rest."

"Thank God! We can live on this meat for several weeks if I stretch it with boiled hides."

The dog was frantically whining and biting at the carcass, so Mother gave him some of the entrails. As we worked cutting up the meat, Baptiste told us of something he had learned.

"*Señora*, I learn from an old man who was a trapper—I think he live most of his life with Indians—he say if you have a bad sore, you take the stomach of a bear an' put it on the sore an' it will help to make it well. Maybe it can help the arm of the *Señor* Donner?"

"It won't hurt to try it. Cut the stomach out and as soon as—"

"*Mire, el lobo*," Baptiste hissed at us.

We turned to see a huge wolf at the top of the snow peering over the edge. He'd planted himself with legs wide apart, his head bobbing up and down, tongue lolling, as he tried to decide if he could jump in and grab some of the meat. We screamed. Mother picked up a piece of wood and hurled it at the wolf, but he ducked away. In a moment he was back.

"Is the gun charged? Baptiste, shoot him."

"I would kill him, but the meat it tastes like rot. Let us finish the work. Tomorrow I will think about killing the wolves."

"Then I will do it." Mother picked up the rifle and swung it shakily in the direction of the wolf.

Baptiste jumped. "*Señora! Por favor, tome cuidado!*"

Then a deafening roar. The discharge of the gun blasted into the snowbank, shooting sharp particles everywhere, the acrid smoke stinging our eyes and throats. Mother stood up on tiptoes, trying to look over the edge. "Did I get him?"

"No, *Señora*, you got nothing. He is gone."

"He'll be back and he'll come down here, to our door. Kill him!"

"Tomorrow is better. I will hide an' wait for him. For his dinner he will have lead."

That evening we sat around the fire, each roasting their own strip of bear meat. Mother made a stew from a large bone, inner bark from the pine tree and cattail roots, and sent the older girls over to Aunt Betsey's camp with food and an invitation to come to Christmas dinner.

"Tell the boys to carry a rifle. That wolf might attack one of the little ones, he's so bold," said Father.

Mrs. Wolfinger knew the talk was of wolves. *"Die Wölfe, ich hasse den Geruch! Es macht mich wahnsinnig!"*

"I think she's saying the sound of the wolves makes her crazy," said Father.

"I hate it too," said Mother. "I want Baptiste to kill those that keep coming around. I'm afraid of them."

When they came back Solomon and William were with them, eager to hear about the successful hunt.

"The mother bear, she no see me, but she hear the sound of my gun an' she see the smoke," said Baptiste. "She roar an' she come for me so I climb the tree fast. She is *muy alta* when she stand an' try to reach me but I climb higher. It is a long time, an' she leave."

"Gol-amighty. I'll bet you peed your pants when she came for you," said Solly.

"I was plenty scared, but I no scared that much," said Baptiste.

Dec. 24

Our prayer for food has been answered. Each day I pray to God and ask Him to deliver us from this prison of snow. But I wonder what God's will is in this horrible drama.

This evening it has turned warmer and is beginning to rain and sleet. When I marked this day off on my calendar sadness came over me. My first husband, Mr. Dozier, died on Christmas Eve, fourteen years ago.

The next morning Mrs. Wolfinger and Mother searched through the wagons again for anything that was food. They found several cups of flour still remaining in a flour bag in the bottom of one of the lidded kegs, along with a pound or two of beans in a tin container in a corner of the wagon.

The fragrance of the cooking drew everyone to our hut long before the meal was ready. Mother passed out ample portions of the food. Father stood up. "Let's give thanks."

Everyone bowed their heads. Mother peeked at us to see if we were behaving properly and we were, kind of. We had our heads down, but were nibbling at our food at the same time.

"Almighty and gracious God, we thank you for providing this supply of food and for this fine young man, Juan Baptiste, who has brought in the food. Watch over and protect us as we wait out these terrible storms. Lord, help us to remain strong. Amen."

"I know there must be a God, but mostly I think the God he sends the bad luck," said Juan Baptiste. "It is good that I kill the bear an' we have food, but why are we to starve in the first place? What we do that the God decide we must suffer?"

"It's a matter of faith," replied Father. "We are here for a purpose that we as mortals cannot see. We must have faith that in the end, it's for the best."

"I think there ain't no God," said William. "If there is, he don't leave civilization. He stays back to home doin' fer people that's smart enough not to journey to California. Auntie Tamsen, this is the most wonderful meal I ever et. What is this potato-like stuff?"

"Remember when those Indians visited our camp and gave us some roots? It's just a starchy vegetable."

"Oh no!" cried Solomon. "Thank God I haven't eaten mine yet!"

"Whatever is the matter with you? It's good. I'll eat yourn if'n you don't want it," said Aunt Betsey.

"Recollect when that Injun gave us some 'a those roots? He was eatin' the heads off'n grasshoppers an' chewin' on these roots. I didn't cotton to the grasshoppers, but I et the roots. All night I had terr'ble stomach pains an' had to run fer the bushes. The Injun came back the next day an' offered more roots, expectin' to share beef an' biscuits with us again. I had a hard time of it to make 'em mind those roots made me sick."

Solomon stood up and demonstrated the "sign" language he used to convince the Indian that the roots were a problem for him.

"I pointed at them roots, then I bent over, holding my belly an' groanin'. Then I pointed to my rear an' made sounds an' the Injun understood me perfect!"

"Probably this small quantity would not have any effect," said Mother. "Even so it would be beneficial."

We all looked at the little lump of root on our plates. Father slipped his to the dog who gulped it down.

Mother looked at Father. "He's eaten Frances's shoes and perhaps it'll help in the process of getting them through him."

"All night he was chewing on the bear fur," said Elitha. "If the shoes don't kill him, that fur will."

Mother and Aunt Betsey had made mittens and stockings for everyone and dolls for the little ones. We were thrilled with the snowshoes Baptiste made for us and stomped around in the snow trying them out. Later, Mother told stories and Father read the Bible.

"It's been long enough," said Father. "Reed should be comin' any day now, it's been plenty of time."

"Reed, his family at the other camps. Maybe he only help them, an' he no come here to help us," said Juan Baptiste. "Maybe he is here already an' the rest of them, they all go."

"He wouldn't do that, Baptiste. He'll come," said Mother.

Baptiste threw the stick he was whittling into the fire. "I think that I go see."

Jan 2, 1847
It was fair today, water dripping everywhere. The winter drags on. Each day I take the bear's stomach from George's arm and wash the arm and put the piece back. His arm looks a little better but he is very weak. I do not know what is sustaining him, as he insists I give the children most of his food. I am terribly worried, but I cannot show it. Oh, God, give me strength.

At night the coyotes and wolves would compete in a yipping and howling contest on the mountain. We didn't mind the coyote sounds, but the wolves filled us with dread and terror. Finally Baptiste made a bait and laid out over several days, managing to kill two wolves. He tied the carcasses to trees on each side of our hut. The dried bodies would swing in the wind, heads dangling, mouths frozen in fanged snarls.

The end of the first week in January, Milt Elliott and Eliza Williams, the Reed's hired girl, came to our camp. We welcomed the company, because we were anxious to hear news from the other camp. Any change in routine relieved our boredom.

"Oh, Miz Donner," said Eliza, "it be the worse kind of fate we have. Miz Reed, Virginia an' Milt an' me, we tried to go over the mountain a few days ago an' we like to froze to death. We couldn't find our way an' had to come back."

Eliza spoke in a strange flat voice that was hard to understand. We'd asked Mother why Eliza talked funny.

"It's because she is almost deaf. But if she can see a person's mouth when talking, she can make out most of what is said."

"Baylis died in December," said Eliza. "Went into a delirium like an' was gone. Now I have nobody."

"We heard about your brother, Eliza. I'm sorry."

"Charlie Burger died a week or two back," said Milt. "Several are in a bad way, too weak to get around. Breen's been sufferin' from the gravels. His boys get wood an' help the others."

"We've had only boiled hides to eat," said Eliza. "I jes' can't eat that gluey stuff, I throws it up. Miz Reed tol' me hides was all she had an' I'd have to live or die on 'em. The Graves's got meat still, but they ain't sharing it. Do you have any food at all?"

"We have a little bear meat and I still have some cattail roots," said Mother. "They make a tolerable stew with a little meat. We must look out for Jacob's family now and we must be very careful with our stores."

Mother handed Eliza a cup of tea. "I've made you some tea. It's soothing to one's nerves and will help you forget about food. It has a little sustenance, too."

"Thank you kindly, missus, but there ain't nothin' that's goin' to keep me from thinkin' about food. I'll drink this an' some of yer coffee will taste good too."

"I'll have some of your coffee, ma'am," said Milt.

"The coffee helps get us through the day," said Father. "That'n

tobacco. Smokin' my pipe is just about the only comforting thing left."
He handed Milt a sack of tobacco. "Got a pipe with you, Milford?"

"Yessir. Thank you kindly."

Milt filled his pipe and got it going. The smell of the burning
tobacco was sharp and good.

Milt took out his knife and began whittling on a piece of wood.
"Keeps my hands busy. I'll make fire startin's fer you, Miz Donner."

Everyone was quiet for a while, sipping their drink, the men
puffing on their pipes. Milt stripped off small yellow-white pieces of
wood onto the floor in front of him. He cleared his throat. "I feel
bad that I can't do nothin' to help Miz Reed an' the children. It's my
fault that Mr. Reed had to leave them. If'n I hadn't got to arguin' with
Snyder, if I'd just waited instead of tryin' to drive the wagon past—"
His face twisted in anguish. "It's a hard burden to bear, thinkin' I'm
responsible."

"Milt, it wasn't your fault," said Mother. "You weren't responsible
for Snyder's anger—he was. You weren't responsible for James drawing a knife and plunging it into the man—James was. The whole matter could have been just a small annoyance, but something in James
triggered a murderous impulse. If he had backed off and left Snyder
alone, it would not have happened. You followed the correct path by
stepping aside. He did not. You cannot blame yourself."

Milt nodded his head. "My pap always used to tell me that fightin's
somethin' you do when you've tried everythin' else, an' I think I've
followed that. But it eats at me." He puffed on his pipe for a while,
then continued. "We've done gone through the four oxen Missus Reed
bought from Breen an' Graves. The company agreed to look out for
the family, but none of 'em will help her, leastways they won't part with
any food."

"That Miz Graves is mean as a stewed witch," said Eliza. "Miz
Reed went to get the hides off'n her cabin an' Miz Graves wouldn't let
her take 'em. She told Miz Reed she has to pay fer the two oxen she got

from her before she can have her goods."

"Hard times can make a person say things they don't really mean," said Mother.

"Mrs. Graves is nice," said Leanna.

"Well, you ain't had to live rubbing elbows with her like we have. Miz Reed, she ain't accustomed to have to make do or not get her way. You know, it's strange," said Eliza, "but Miz Reed, so weak an' frail like with those terr'ble headaches, she don't have 'em anymore, leastways that I notice."

"That's right, she don't," said Milt. "I guess God just up an' cured her, 'cause she has to look out fer the children an' all by herself."

"I no think *Dios* he cure her," said Baptiste. "She no has the husband to feel sorry for her, so it no good to have the headache."

"We've still not found all of our oxen," said Father. "We keep hopin' for a good thaw so's they'll start showin'. We found several, but we've used 'em up now. They were poor, mostly skin and bones. If we could find 'em we could share some with you. I cain't do a gol-durned thing, I'm weak as a kitten. If it wasn't for Baptiste, we'd have a mighty hard time."

"Some of 'em's talkin' about usin' the dead fer food," said Milt. "They ain't come to it yet." Milt paused and cleared his throat. "I dunno. I think I'd rather pass on from starvation than ... " His voice trailed away and he stared into the fire for a while, then continued whittling on his stick.

"Things are that bad then?"

"With some of 'em, it is. Graves still has some meat, an' Breen, but the rest of us is livin' on hides. I got the last of Missus Reed's meat from Breen two days before Christmas. We've eaten all the dogs that were still with us."

"The only dog we still had disappeared a few days after Christmas," said Father. "He was such skin and bones, he wouldn't have made much of a meal anyway."

Father chuckled. "That brings to mind that preacher that was with us early on—he told a story 'bout some people that'd come back East the year before we left. They'd had all their goods stolen by the Indians an' were in a sorry way, when one of 'em kills a skunk an' it was all they had to eat. One of the group was a minister and when they sat down to dinner with this skunk the main course, the minister starts to say the blessing. The other man gets all hot, an' refused, sayin' he wasn't goin' to stand fer any blessin' bein' said over a dad-blamed skunk. He told the minister he'd be better to save his blessin's until they got some deer meat or somethin' fit to eat!" Father looked at Mother. "I'm not sure what his message was—"

"That one should be grateful and thank God for whatever comes to the table, I guess, but I am glad that for us it was a bear instead of a skunk."

Baptiste got up from where he was sitting cross-legged on the floor and began to work on the fire, poking and gathering the coals. The damp wood sizzled in defiance as he added more sticks.

"You know the *Señor* Kit Carson? He tell me that one time he eat the man meat. He was in the camp of the Crow Indians an' he did not know this. They make the fool with him. He said the meat was *chungo*—" Baptiste paused and muttered to himself. "*Que es el Inglés?* Uh, rope. It was … like rope."

Baptiste shrugged. "Maybe it was an old one. He say the color was strange, kind of white. I do not know if he tell me the truth."

"Baptiste," cried Elitha, "you're making me sick!"

"I only say what someone tell me."

"It is not a good thing to contemplate," said Mother, "If we should reach a point where we have no other food, what would we do?"

"I would rather die!" exclaimed Elitha.

"You ate the mouse I catch. How much is the difference?" asked Baptiste.

Father frowned and raised his hand, signaling Baptiste not to say anything more. We were silent, the only sound for a few moments was the fire murmuring at the wood and the scratch, scratch of a branch against the frozen hides on the top of our hut.

"Elitha, Leanna," said Mother, "go over to Aunt Betsey's and ask them to come. They'll enjoy a change of scene and talking to our visitors." Elitha groaned. "No argument, Elitha. It will be good for all of you to get out."

"I go with them," said Baptiste. "I take the *Señora* Betsey some wood."

The girls bundled up and then helped Baptiste load some wood on a buffalo skin. We could hear their chatter fade away as they went off. Mother decided to serve the meal in her good dishes and we washed them for her. She gave everyone a cup of soup with a chunk of bear meat, a small piece of pine-tree bread, and a square of the tallow she'd tried out from boiling the bones and scraps from the bear.

"What is this stuff?" asked Eliza. She held up the square of pine bark.

"It's from the cambium—the inner bark of the pine tree. Tell the people over there about it. You can only get a small amount from each tree. It has sustenance, at least it can help keep one from starving if you can get enough."

"It don't taste bad, kind'a sweet," said Milt.

"Well, I used the last bit of my molasses in these. If you mix it with fat, that helps."

"I hanker for salt powerful bad. We ain't had no salt at all since that you gave me last time I was here."

"We will share what food we have with you for a few days, but we won't be able to feed you longer. Surely the Graves family or the Breen family will give you something," Mother told them.

Eliza started crying. "The Breens have plenty of meat, but they won't share."

"They did take in Virginia," said Milt. "So at least maybe she's getting some food."

"That don't help us none." Eliza snuffled for a while, poking at the fire with a stick, raising sparks that blew upward in the dark.

"Listen, I think the wind's changed," said Father, "it's coming from the northwest. Likely it's goin' to storm again."

"The blamed storms never stop," growled Milt.

"I don't hate anythin' in this world as much as I hate snow," said Betsey, "an' the wind."

Milt got up and pulled open the door. A blast of cold, moist air showered us with tiny sharp particles of ice. He quickly closed it.

"Well," said Eliza, "we cain't leave 'til it stops snowing anyways."

One day I was playing in the doorway and became fascinated by a sunbeam that I saw on the floor of the hut. It was a bright little ray and I sat down under it, holding it on my lap. When I moved my hands through it, it broke into, and jumped and flitted from one place to another.

I was so taken with this little toy that I wanted to show it to Mother, so I caught it up in my apron and went to her. "Mama, I have something to show you. It's so pretty, I hope we can put it in a jar to keep." I carefully opened my apron. "It's gone!"

I looked all over the floor but couldn't find it. I explained to Mother what it was and took her by the hand to the doorway so she could help me look for it, but it was just as the last ray disappeared.

"I hope it comes back again. Will it?"

"Yes, if there is sun again."

By mid-January the snow was twelve to fourteen feet deep in the drifts. One clear day Father sent Baptiste to the other camps to see how they were faring. He found they were in bad shape, same as we were. Several had died and several others were in such a pitiful condition that they would likely die soon. They were very short of food, living mostly on the boilings from hides. The Breen family had taken in Mrs. Reed and her children when the hides that covered her shanty were needed for food.

It was wet in our tents for days on end. Sometimes Baptiste could not get wood and we had no fire. The snow covered us so deep that little daylight entered.

We were weak and lethargic, curling up in bed, trying to get warm. But on days when the clouds cleared and the sun shone upon our world, our mood lifted, and we would warm ourselves outside. We'd gaze at the mountains hoping to see rescuers. Baptiste would climb a tree and stayed many hours there looking for the men and listening for the halloos.

"They must come soon, or we will die," said Baptiste to Mother. She frowned at him. "They will come soon, and we will leave," she said. "Yes, surely, they will come soon."

We tramped over to the other camp to see Aunt Betsey and the children. Mother was appalled at how weak and listless they all were. "Betsey," she said, "the sun is wonderful today. Bring the children out for a while. They need the light. Solomon, you and William get out and get your mother some wood."

Pushing and prodding, she finally got them outside. The two older boys poked around and found a few limbs sticking out of the snow, but as soon as they'd drug them close to the hut, they disappeared back inside the hut.

"Solomon, that is not enough wood. You boys go right back out there until you have a supply for a week or two."

"Aw, get Baptiste to do it."

Picking up one of the limbs, Mother swung it at Solomon and then William.

"Get out there. Now."

On good days Mother had us all help take clothes and bedding outside and drape the things over a line to dry, and we would clean and renew our hut.

"Mother, why do we have to work when we're so tired?" complained Georgia.

"I'm dizzy and weak when I get up," said Leanna.

"You must keep active or you won't be strong to walk when the rescuers come to take us out."

"It hurts me," whined Frances.

"Yes, and it hurts me too, but I want to stay strong so I move about as much as I can and you must also. Look, it's so pretty today, we don't want to spoil it by moping around. Let's finish the work and then we'll have a tea party. Tonight I will plan a special time and I have a surprise, a treat."

"What is the treat?" I asked.

"Wait and see. When it is dark Baptiste will build a fire and we'll have our party outside."

"Mother, it's freezing. Can't we do it inside?"

"We'll bundle up. Believe me, it will be all right."

Thoughts of the treat—maybe something to eat!—fired us with a more enthusiasm and we became more cheerful. Baptiste built the fire early and by dark it had enough coals to heat a kettle of water. There was much grumbling, but after Mother told us that only the ones who were outside would participate in the surprise, we trooped outside.

Mother showed us a jar. "Yesterday when I was going through a trunk I found this. Do you remember back home in the winter, we would all gather and play games and have music, and make popcorn in the fireplace?"

"Mother, Mother, is that popcorn?"

"Yes. We can make two kettles. Baptiste will take one to Aunt Betsey and your cousins."

When all the corn had popped, Baptiste placed the kettle on some sticks of wood before us. Mother gave a bowl of popcorn to each one.

"Eat very, very slowly and drink lots of tea. We don't want to have stomach aches."

We took the kernels one by one and chewed slowly around the edges, popping the last bit in our mouths before taking another.

"Baptiste, I'll make the other kettle and then you can take it to Betsey."

When Baptiste came back, Mother told everybody to look up at the sky and she would teach us to read the stars and to recognize the North Star. It seemed to me that the stars were so close I could touch them.

"First you must be able to find the Little Dipper. You know the Big Dipper already, don't you?" We nodded our heads.

"Then you find the two stars that make up the Little Dipper's handle. These two stars are called the pointer stars. The North Star lies above these two stars in a line about five times the distance between the pointer stars. Does anyone see the Little Dipper?"

"I see it, " exclaimed Frances. "But I don't see the North Star."

Mother pulled her shawl tighter around her shoulders and leaned forward. "It's a very large and bright star, and stays in one place, always to the north. From it you know which way is north. There is an Indian legend that explains why the North Star stands still. It seems there was an Indian named Na-Gah who tried to impress his father by climbing the tallest cliff he could find. He climbed and climbed until one day he found himself at the top of a very high mountain—"

"As tall as these mountains?" asked Georgia.

"Oh, much higher. The mountain was so tall that Na-Gah looked down on all the other mountains, but unfortunately, there was no way down. When his father looked for him, he found Na-Gah stuck high above. He didn't want his son to suffer because of his bravery, so he turned Na-Gah into a star. It is called the Pole Star, or Polaris, because the earth's axis always points to it in the northern sky."

"I know this," said Baptiste. "I learn this by a man I travel with."

"It's called celestial navigation," said Mother.

"Mother, how did you know about the stars?"

"I was taught navigation and surveying by my father, your grandfather."

"What is surveying?"

"That is when you learn how to find directions and how to mark off boundaries for each farm so that they can keep everything in order and property can be sold or transferred."

Mother stood up. "Let's go in. Baptiste, please put these coals in the kettle and take them in. We'll warm our hands over the kettle and heat some stones for our feet before we get in bed."

Jan. 31

It froze very hard last night, and today is cloudy, no sun to cheer us. Another dreary month has passed and I worry constantly that we will not survive to see another unless help comes over the mountain.

Surely the party that left in December has reached the settlements. Help must be on the way, it is past time. Oh, God, I am so afraid. Give me the strength to keep my family alive.

Chapter Eleven

In mid-February, a rescue party
came from California

"*Señora! Veo a los hombres! Señora*, it is men from California. Three men are coming!"

We were outside, preparing to wash clothes when we heard Baptiste yelling. He came to the top of the snow steps. "It's men coming!"

We all started toward the men, waving and yelling, sinking down into the soft snow and falling as we tried to pull our feet out to take another step. Mother took off her shawl and waved it in the air.

"We are here. Men, men ..." Baptiste shouted.

"Oh God, do they see us? Do they see us?"

"*Si, Señora*. They come."

We were in such excitement and anticipation that it seemed hours before the men came close. Walking in the lead was a man who, with all his winter clothing on, looked to be about as broad as he was tall, his face red and chapped, his lips cracked and sore from exposure.

"Miz Donner? I'm John Rhodes. We sure been worried about you people, and it seems, rightly so."

"Yes, I'm Mrs. George Donner. We are very glad to see you. You weren't able to bring horses?"

"No, ma'am. No way can horses, or any livestock, get over the snow. We brung what food we could carry in. Most of it we cached back along the trail to use on the way out."

"Well, we're happy to have what you've brought. Please come in and talk to my husband. He's suffering from weakness caused by an injury to his hand."

Mr. Rhodes turned and pointed to the other men. "Miz Donner, this is Sep Moultrie an' the man coming up is Reason Tucker. His foot's been frostbit. He's needin' some doctorin' on it. Men, this is Miz Donner, George's wife."

They nodded their heads. "Ma'am."

"You've got another family here?"

"Yes, Mr. Rhodes, Jacob's family, George's brother." Mother pointed. "Their camp is just over there."

"I take the men there," said Baptiste.

Mr. Rhodes instructed Mr. Moultrie and Mr. Tucker to proceed on to Aunt Betsey's camp and give her some of the food they had brought. We went inside our hut.

"Were you able to bring horses?" asked Father.

"No, sir, Mr. Donner. We couldn't bring 'em up any farther than the snow line. Sure wish we could've, it would have been easier on us."

Mr. Rhodes went on to explain that only those who were strong enough to walk could be taken out. "There's several from the lake camps that aren't strong enough to go," he said. "We're gonna try to carry out some of the children. We haven't the men to carry more, but another rescue party will be along in a short while. That is, if it quits storming. If it don't quit, well, it'll take 'em longer. We'll leave what we can spare in the way of provisions."

Aunt Betsey came to our camp, crying and wringing her hands. Her face was gray and gaunt, her body nothing but angular bones.

"I would go, but they won't take my little ones an' I cain't leave them. William and George can go. What did they tell you?"

"They can't take our three little ones either, Betsey, but Leanna and Elitha are strong enough, and Mrs. Wolfinger. We'll have to wait for the next relief."

"Why cain't those men each carry a child?"

"It might weaken them to the point that they couldn't make it and both would die," said Mother.

"What have we done to deserve this?" cried Betsey. "If God loves us like the preachers say, why ain't he watching out fer us? What kind of a God would allow this to happen?" She collapsed on the floor, wailing.

"Elizabeth. Elizabeth, listen," said Father. "There's always a picture that we, as mortals, can't see. Dyin's not that bad. We're all goin' to end that way anyway. We'll all be together again in the after-life."

"That's supposed to make me feel better, watching my children suffer an' starve?" she asked between sobs. "Nothin' to give but hide boilin's, their little hands beggin' for somethin', anythin'. They ain't leavin' enough food to keep us alive fer more'n a day or two. I told that Mr. Tucker that if'n we didn't find our animals under the snow by then, we'd have to start diggin' up the dead bodies for food." Betsey put her hands over her face and began sobbing again. "What have we come to?"

"We still have hides," said Mother.

"They cain't eat that glue. They're weak an' sick, look like death. I got to do it."

"Betsey, the teas that I make do help sustain—"

"I don't like them teas. I drink the coffee an' I give it to the young'uns, they like it better."

Mother helped Betsey get up. "Betsey, I'll make some soup from the meat the men have brought. I'll bring it over. You need to get the children ready to go."

"Tamsen, do you recollect, just after we left home, that swarm of gnats that got into our bread dough an' turned it black?"

"Yes, we threw it away."

"I was thinkin' of it all day yesterday. I'd eat it now an' be glad. I'd give everything I have for that pan of bread dough. I'd be happy to just have the crumbs we swept off the table at home."

She sighed deeply and fidgeted with the edge of her apron. "Did you talk to Juan Baptiste? He's wantin' to go, he tol' me."

"George promised him if he would stay that he would always have a home with us in California. He's agreed to stay."

Mother dressed Elitha and Leanna in as many layers of clothing as they could wear and provided each with a blanket to use as a shawl in the day and a cover at night. When they were ready to go, they went to Father to say good-bye.

"I know it's hard, but think about how wonderful it will be in California. We'll be along as soon as we can. Mother, do they have money?"

"Yes, I sewed it in their cloaks. Elitha, do not let people know you have it or they might take it from you. It is enough to keep you until we can join you. You must be brave."

Leanna began to cry. "We don't want to go. We want to wait until we can all go together."

"You'll be with people you know. Noah will be with you, and Mrs. Wolfinger, and William and George, and the Reed family."

"Girls, come here, sit down," said Father. They sat beside him on the bed, clutching their reticules, tears streaming down their faces.

"You'll just be gettin' to California before the rest of us. There's more rescuers comin' an' spring will be here before long. They'll bring mules to carry us out. It's just a temporary thing. You're both old enough to be alone for a little while, aren't you?"

They nodded their heads and wiped the tears from their eyes. "Yes, Father, we'll try."

"Come along, girls," said Mother, "The men are anxious to go."

We went outside to see them off, even Father. Mr. Rhodes stood, bending over as he tried to shift his pack higher on his back.

"Miz Donner, I tol' Baptiste that he needs to stay 'cause you ain't got anybody to get yer wood an' such—he got some surly with me."

"He'll stay, Mr. Rhodes. Will you deliver our girls to Mr. Sutter?"

"Ma'am, I will do my best. Another relief should be here in a few days."

"Elitha," said Mother, "look out for Leanna, she's not as strong as you are."

"I know. I'll help her."

We watched them move off, the strongest in the lead and each thereafter stretching to step in the footsteps of the one before. They kept turning to look back, waving again and again, until they disappeared from view. Heavy of heart, we remained outside. We sat on Baptiste's blanket atop the snow.

"Now, be *ángelitas* an—"

"What's a an-hal-ito?" asked Frances.

"Is an angel! Now, be silent and I will tell you a story an' also I will teach you words in *español*."

"*Sí!*" We all choroused. Batiste had taught us some words of the Spanish language. We knew that *está bien* meant "all right" and *español* meant "spanish".

"*Mi Papá*, he was a trapper an' hunter an' so I was too. He was a very strong man, as men must be who go to the mountains. *Hombre muy fuerte. Comprenden?*"

Another chorus of "*sí, sí*".

"That is very good. *Muy bien! Mi papá*, he went deep into the lands of the Indians an' took the furs. Sometimes the Indians, they find the trappers an' many they kill in ways that were terrible."

"Did they kill your papa?"

"Yes, I think it was so. *Mi pápa*, he go on the fur hunt an' he never come back."

"What did you do?"

"I was very young an' I was raised by *mi abuela*, my grandmother. She is a Spanish lady, a lady of worth. I hope to return to see her before she die, but first I must go to California an' see for myself what it is that is there. Since I have nine years I work. I work here an' there, I hunt the furs, I work on the freight wagons. One day a great company of men came to our village. The leader was the Captain Frémont. I hear that his expedition is going to the Pacific Ocean an' I say to *mi abuela*, I will go to him an' offer myself an' I will travel to far-off places. I will tell him that I speak the language of the Utah an' I know the language of signs."

"What's that?" asked Frances.

"The language of signs is when you talk with your hands instead of your mouth. This language is known by all Indians an' many white men."

"I would like to talk with my hands instead of my mouth. Leanna says that I am too loud." Frances burst into tears. "But Leanna's gone—"

"I didn't want 'Litha an' 'Anna to go," I said, and I began to cry.

"You must not cry. They are going where there is no snow an' the sun shines an' there is food to eat. They are going to be happy! Now, Frémont, he had a very large company of men an' horses. When they came to my village, they wanted to buy food, but there was no food to sell. So they camped an' men were sent to the fort of the *Señor* Bent to buy supplies. That is when I talk to the *Señor* Carson. He ask me if I know the work of horses."

Baptiste stood up, pounding his chest. *"Por supuesto! Soy el mejor!* I am the best! I no need to speak the *Inglés* because *Señor* Carson, he know the *español muy bien."*

"They engage me to care for the horses, but I hunt too. Sometimes I trap for furs. One time when I was trapping, Indians they come by the stream where I am. They no see me, but they see where I walk. They were the Utah. I know they will find me, so I go in the water. My traps they are upstream, so I go downstream. When I leave the water I was almost frozen, but I find a bear cave. Can you guess what was in the cave?"

"A bear?"

"Yes! A big mama bear and a cub."

"Did they growl at you and eat you?"

"I am here, so how the bear eat me up? No, they were in their winter sleep. My wet clothes, I take them off an' I lay near that mama bear, and I am a little warm. I stay there for two days an' then I think the Indians they are gone an' I go out of the cave. The Indians they steal my traps an' I no could hunt the furs anymore. I go back to the *Señor* Frémont's party. They no let me in camp."

"Why not?"

"They say I stink. They make me go in the stream an' wash an' they throw my clothes away. What they give me was old an' it no fit me. But I have Old Navajo."

He patted the blanket on which we sat. "I trade for this blanket when I was at the fort of the *Señor* Bent."

"We like Old Navajo. We're glad you still have it," said Frances.

"With Frémont the work was hard an' the food, *no buena*. I decide I go to California by myself. That is how I meet your *papá y mamá* at the Fort Bridger."

Father got up to go inside. "Baptiste, you tell a good story," he said. "Mother, do you have any willow bark left?"

"Yes, I'll make you some tea. We'll come in too." Mother always looked worried when she looked at Father, and we were worried too.

"Frances," said Mother, "start taking some of those warm stones from the fire."

Mother always tried her best to make Father comfortable. She warmed stones by the fire to put around him on top of his blanket.

"Baptiste, would you bring in some hard snow? I want to cool Mr. Donner's arm, perhaps it will help the pain."

Father yelped when Mother put the ice around his arm.

"Oh, honey, I'm sorry. If you can stand it for a minute it should numb the pain."

"Yeah. It helps. I'm just a cry-baby."

"I think you have every right to flinch. I wish I could do something that would help."

"You've done everythin' you can. It's just not gonna get better. You've got to face up to it. You an' the children need to go to the other camp to be ready for the next relief. I ain't gonna make it, Tamsen, we both know it."

"George, hush. I will not leave you here alone. That is all there is to it."

We sat on the edge of the bed while Father sipped his tea. "This stuff is god-awful," he complained.

"It's worth it to feel better, George."

"I'm not sure about that."

"George, tomorrow I want you to move to the bed beside the fire. It will be warmer and more cheerful."

"And I want you to take the girls to the other camp, ready for the next relief."

And so we waited. Juan Baptiste would take us outside on nice days and we would help him with his chores. Mother would sit outside, writing in her journal or sketching. At night Mother would knit and tell stories and we would talk of our family back in the States.

"Mother, where is your mother and father?"

"They lived in Newburyport, Massachusetts, where I was born. My father, William Eustis, passed on—it's now four years. My mother's name was Tamsen Wheelwright. She died when I was young. and Father married a kindly woman. I loved her like I did my own mother."

"Your mother's name was Tamsen too?"

"Yes. I had a good education, and I want you to have the same—to use your minds and be independent. I loved to learn, so it was natural that I become a teacher."

"Mother, tell us the story again about those grouchy men at your school," asked Frances.

"That was at my first school in Illinois. I went to Illinois to help Uncle William because his wife had passed on.

Then I took a teaching position nearby. I had a wonderful class of students, but a problem developed. The men who were in charge of the school did not like it that I would knit while the lessons were progressing. They felt I couldn't apply myself to teaching if I was distracted by knitting.

"I invited the men to come in, observe the class and then pronounce if the lessons proceeded in good fashion. They did so and afterwards they agreed that the children were receiving a full measure of my teaching skills.

"You see, I stood up for what I believed was right. I want you to always keep in mind that you must do what is right and always stand up for what you believe. If someone is not being fair to you, you must let them know you will not tolerate it."

"Mama, you'll make people be fair to us."

"You might be leaving the mountains before your father and I. You would be among strangers for awhile."

"Why can't we go together?"

"Because your father is too weak to walk and we must wait for horses so that he can ride. I must stay to help him.

"But remember, when anyone asks you who you are, always answer that you are the children of Mr. and Mrs. George Donner and don't forget, you must always be polite and mannerly because strangers might not have a lot of patience with children."

Feb. 24

The days drag on and on, gray, monotonous, cold. Only the wild, sad wind has life. Now and again we are relieved by days when the sun shines, but they are bittersweet days because the snow melts and the water drips down on us, wetting everything. Yesterday it was so nice it seemed like early spring, but today is cloudy and the wind blows hard from the west. I fear we will not survive much longer if help does not arrive soon. I try to keep the girls well, I must keep them alive! Oh, God! Spare my children!

We had no food except the boilings from hides and some tallow. One day Baptiste brought something wrapped in a cloth and put it on the table.

"*Señora*, I bring you this food. The *niñas*, they must have more than the boilings you make or they will sicken soon. And me, I no keep strong to do the work eating only glue from the hides, so I use this, and *Señora* Betsey, she use it too. One day, when I climb the tree to cut off the branches, I see the wolves. They are digging the men out of the snow an' already a leg of—"

He looked at us, and then back to Mother.

"I think that we have no food an' meat is meat. The soul that was there, it is gone, only the dead body is left. Like the deer, the buffalo. Is there difference?"

"I don't know."

"I have to fight the wolves. I am much afraid, but I hit at them with a heavy stick an' they move away, but not far. I dig out one of the men an' I drag him to the old hut. There is no one there anyway. *Señora*, there is no other way to survive."

"Baptiste, you can get more of the pine bark."

"Only a little can I get this way. I have taken from all the trees around here. It is much work an' I am getting weak. It is all my strength to get the wood for the fires."

"Baptiste, it's all right," said Father from his bed. "Mother, there's no other way."

We went to Baptiste's camp and he cooked some of the meat for us. "It's one of those men, isn't it?" asked Frances.

"It is meat, and you are very hungry. What does it matter?"

It was two weeks after the last rescue party had left that the next party of rescuers came to our camp. We were outside when we saw three men approaching. Mother struggled through the snow to greet them.

"Are there more men coming?"

"Yes'm, Mr. Reed and some others'll be comin' on shortly. I'm Cady, this here's Stone. The man comin' up is Clark. He seen some bear sign. Soon's he leaves his pack he's goin' after the bear."

"You have food for us?"

The men shrugged off their packs, took out a package and handed it to Mother.

"This is all that you have brought?"

"Yes'm, we done cached most up on the mountain to use on the way out."

"Please take part of this to Jacob's family." Mother pointed in the direction of Aunt Betey's hut where only a wisp of smoke showed above the snow.

Juan Baptiste had been gathering wood when he'd heard the men's voices. He rushed back to camp as the men were making their way to Aunt Betsey's hut.

"Only three men? How they carry the children?"

"They say more men are coming."

Later that day, Mr. Reed, with several other men, came to our camp. Mother greeted him.

"James. How good it is to see you."

"How are you? How is George?"

"George is not well. Please, come in."

Mr. Reed followed us inside, pausing while his eyes adjusted to the gloom.

"George, James is here." Mother helped Father sit up. He put out his hand to Mr. Reed.

"Oh, James, it's good to see you. Have you brought mules?"

"No, we couldn't get through with horses or mules. The snow on top is twenty to thirty feet deep. I apologize for the lateness of my arrival here in the mountains. It was most difficult to get over."

"Do you have news of my daughters?" asked Father. "They went out with the first party."

"Yes, yes, they are safe. I met that party as we were coming up. My wife and children also. They are all on their way to Mr. Sutter's now."

"Your family? Are they all right?" asked Mother.

"Yes, thank God, my family is safe. Mrs. Reed and two of the children are now on their way out and the other two, Patty and Thomas, they're still at the lake but all right. I cannot tell you how distressed I am for what has happened. It is a most terrible situation."

Mother brought a chair for Mr. Reed and he set it close to Father. Mr. Reed was very emotional, and it was several moments before he could continue.

"George, it was very difficult to move over the snow and fight the constant storms. Even now we are worried whether or not we will be able to get the people out. It is a good distance to an elevation where there is no snow. My group is too small to take children that cannot walk. It is extremely arduous—"

"James," exclaimed Mother, "the other men promised us the next party would take our children out! The men who came this morning brought little food. We cannot survive much longer!"

"There is another much larger party following me and they will be able to take them. I will leave as much food as I can. Hopefully it will be enough to last you until they arrive."

"Only a few days?"

"A week at the most. Of course, that depends on the weather. Mr. Sutter told me that this has been a most unusual course of storms."

Mr. Reed got up from his chair. "I must see to the other family. I can't express how sorry I am about Jacob. I'll come again before we leave, but we must make haste. I'm leaving men here to care for you until the next relief arrives."

We followed Mother and Mr. Reed outside, squinting against the white glare from the snow.

"We're all suffering greatly from the effects of this brightness on our eyes. I want you to know that as soon as I arrived in California—and it was a hellacious journey—I worked diligently to form up a relief party. I could not obtain men as the rebellions and wars took most of the able men away from the area. Mr. McCutcheon and I made an attempt in November, but the deep snow prevented us from ascending and we had to turn back." His voice trembled. "As God is my witness, I have done everything I could do."

We walked toward the other camp on the narrow path carved in the snow.

"Betsey and her little ones are in a bad way," said Mother. "I know you've done everything you could, James, but I'm afraid it's too late."

We heard the crunching of boots on the snow coming toward us and recognized Hiram Miller.

"Reed, things are bad over at the other camp," he said. "They's been eatin' the dead. Did you go in that teepee-like hut? The empty one? God have mercy—"

James raised his hand signaling Hiram to stop talking. "Yes, I did. Go ahead and get started on resetting the tents."

Mr. Miller looked surprised when he saw us behind Mr. Reed. "Miz Donner, how you be?"

"As well as can be expected. So you made it to California?"

"Yes'm, but hardly had a chance to collect myself before we started on this expedition."

"Would you visit with George? He'll be so glad to see you—"

Mr. Reed interrupted. "When we get this work done we'll do that, but we must make haste."

We continued on to Aunt Betsey's camp.

"They're taking Mary, Isaac, and Solly but they won't take my little boys," Betsey cried as soon as she saw us. "Oh, God, Tamsen, what am I to do?" She collapsed on the ground, crying pitifully. Mother knelt down next to her.

"James says another relief party will be here in a few days. It's a larger party, they'll be able to carry them out. We need to keep on until they get here."

"Tamsen, I ain't got no strength to keep on. I'm gonna be joining Jacob in the hereafter. But what will happen to my little ones?"

"Betsey, the men are going to reset your tents to make you more comfortable."

Hiram Miller conducted the selling of Jacob's store of goods to some of the rescuers, and they began putting together bundles to carry out.

"Do they mean to carry goods and not help get a child out?" Mother asked Mr. Reed.

"I have no authority over these men. They do as they wish. But I can tell you they have suffered great hardship to get here."

"In other words, they have suffered greatly in order to purchase goods that will make them a lot of money in California. How has that helped relieve us?"

"All of the men have carried in heavy packs of food. Most of it we cached along the way in order to feed the people as we go out. The labor was extremely hard. Some now feel their task has ended. I have arranged for Mr. Cady and Mr. Stone to stay to help you. It should be but a short time before the next group gets here."

We stood on a bank of snow and watched the group of rescuers and rescued until they disappeared.

"Those men, *Señora*, I no like them. Reed, he say I must stay. I do it because you need me, because the *niñas,* they need me. Not because he tell me."

"Baptiste, I am very grateful that you will stay. Mr. Reed says another party is coming soon and we'll all be able to leave."

We went back to Aunt Betsey's tent. We sat on one of the beds, feet dangling, watching as Mother fed our little cousins more of the soup she had made. We could tell that she was very upset. Betsey began crying again. "Tamsen, take care of my babies when—"

"Hush such talk, Betsey. I will do everything I can to help you, but you must not give up. I've got to go back now. Mr. Cady will keep your fire up."

"I heard them two men talking. They's leaving."

Aunt Betsey was right. Mr. Cady and Mr. Stone were growing apprehensive that they were going to be forced to join us in our starved camp.

"Miz Donner, we gotta' leave. We need to catch up with Mr. Reed's party. Our provisions is near gone an' we're a'feared'a bein' trapped here fer days, mebbe weeks 'fore another party kin get over the mountain."

"You were charged with our care."

"We ain't bein' paid to risk our lives, being trapped our ownselves. There be a storm a'coming."

"Then take our girls out with you."

"We'd have to carry 'em an' we cain't."

"I believe they can walk. If you break the snow for them they'll walk in your tracks."

"No. I'm sorry, we cain't take 'em. We'll need to move fast to find Reed."

"I'll give you five hundred dollars if you will take them."

"Well, I dunno. I'll talk to Stone."

In a few minutes he was back. "Ma'am, we'll take 'em if you'll give five hundred fer me, five hundred fer Stone. They'll have ta' walk. We'll leave as soon as they're ready to go. We cain't wait fer Clark."

Georgia and I clung to Mother, wailing. Frances went to Father, burying her head in his blankets.

"Mother, we don't want to go with those men, we don't want to."

"I know, and I don't want you to either. But it is for the best. These men will take you to Elitha and Leanna. They'll watch over you until Father and I can come."

Frances began to cry. "What if you die and we'll never see you again? What if the men never come back for you?"

Mother fell on her knees, holding us. "Oh, God, give me strength." She held us so tightly it hurt.

"Mother, go with them. They need you. It's best," said Father, his voice almost too weak for us to hear. "Tamsen, go with them."

Mother shook her head, and kept crying and begging God to take care of us. Frances slipped off the bed to the floor, wailing. Father reached down and stroked her hair.

"Honey, it's gonna be all right."

What sorrow, what pain.

Mr. Cady came into the hut. "Ma'am, if the children's goin', we got to leave now, it's fixin' to storm."

We cried even louder and clung to Mother tighter. She got to her feet, gently pushing us away.

"Girls, I must get you ready to go."

She dressed us in layers of clothes and our cloaks.

"Frances, where are your shoes?"

"The dog ate them, Mother."

"Oh, yes." Mother searched for shoes and finally put a pair of her own on her. She made a bundle of a few things and asked Mr. Cady to carry it. We went up the steps of packed snow, sniffling, noses running.

Juan Baptiste had just come back from his daily hunt for wood and was surprised to see us leaving.

"The men, they leave? The *niñas* go with them? The *Señor* Clark, he no come back yet. Why they leave? I go too, they will need me."

"These men are stronger than you. They have promised to take good care of them. Baptiste, if Clark leaves, I will have no one to help me."

Baptiste knelt down in the snow and took us into his arms. "*Vaya con Dios, mis anjelitos*. I make promise, you I will find in California. I will be leaving too."

Mother took her handkerchief and wiped our tears. "Try to be brave. We will come as soon as we can. Do not be afraid. God will take care of you."

Chapter Twelve

*The men promised they would
take us to Sutter's Fort, but they
left us at the lake camps.*

We followed the men, one behind the other, stretching our legs to step into the depressions made by their boots. Frances managed better than Georgia and I. Our little legs couldn't reach. We would step part-way between the tracks, one foot sinking down into the soft snow and getting stuck while we were trying to reach the next depression with the other. We tried jumping, but that lasted only a short distance. We fell down, exhausted, crying. Mr. Cady stopped and came back.

"You children, you need to keep up."

"Mr. Cady, we can't step that far." Frances pointed to the tracks.

"We cain't slow down. We have to get over that pass before the storm that's a'coming."

Mr. Cady took my hand, Mr. Stone took Georgia's, and they pulled and lifted us along. "How much farther is it?" we asked every few minutes.

"Hush. It's a long way yet. We're just as tired as you. Jes' sit down here an' rest for minute."

Gratefully collapsing on the snow, we ate some of the beef jerky that Mother had tucked into our pockets. The men went off and we could see that they were arguing.

"I think they're talking about leaving us," said Frances.

"We can go back to Mother and Father," said Georgia.

I began crying. "We don't know how to go back."

"We can follow the tracks we made."

"What if it snows and covers up the tracks? We'll get lost," I wailed, and then Georgia and Frances had to wail too. It was too much for us.

Mr. Cady came back. "C'mon. Let's get movin.' You, little one, I'm gonna try and carry you. Stone's gonna carry my pack."

He hoisted me on his back, my arms around his neck, but put me down after a few steps.

"That ain't a' gonna work, you're choking me."

Then he picked me up and put me over his shoulder, but we hadn't gone very far when I got sick from the jostling and my head being down and threw up.

"Tarnation!" Mr. Cady dumped me down on the snow again.

"I'm s-s-sorry," I wailed.

"I'm blamed wore out," said Mr. Cady.

"You have to walk. Mr. Cady will get mad and leave us," Frances whispered to me.

We struggled on. It was hard for Frances too, because the shoes Mother had given her were too big, coming off her feet when they caught in the snow.

We struggled on and on. The wind began to blow, chapping our faces and hands with it's sharp edges. We tried to keep our hands tucked inside our cloaks, but then it was hard to keep our balance. Pulling our hoods over our faces, we clumped along, peering down at our feet to keep on the path made by the men. We were so numb that we didn't at first realize that we'd reached the other camp. There was a man standing in a doorway.

"These is the Donner children," said Mr. Cady.

"Why are you bringing them here?" asked the man. "You cannot leave them here, there's no one to care for them. The lady here, she can't move from her bed. Take them with you."

Mr. Cady pushed us forward, past the man and into the cabin.

"Keseberg, they's stayin' here."

Mr. Cady turned and walked away. It was very dark inside the cabin and we held on to each other, afraid to move. Then we heard a quavering voice. "Who is it?"

"It's three Donner children. Some men came and left them here," answered Mr. Keseberg.

"Bring them over here," the voice said.

A form came towards us and led us to the back of the cabin, where we could now see a fire glowing and the dim outline of a woman sitting on a bed. "Which Donner children are you?" she asked.

"The children of Mr. and Mrs. George Donner," Frances replied.

"Yes, I see. The three little ones, aren't you?"

"Yes, ma'am, we are."

"Well, this is Simon, the only child I have left."

We now realized the woman was Mrs. Murphy. We edged closer to the fire, shivering in our wet clothes.

"Sit yourselves down," Simon whispered. "Mr. Keseberg is wrathy. Best you stay quiet."

"Simon, help the girls take off their cloaks. Give them one of my blankets to wrap up in."

We huddled together, falling into an exhausted sleep. When we awakened, we could see daylight through cracks in the walls of the cabin. We stirred around, and Simon edged over to us.

"Simon," whispered Frances, "do you have a necessary place? Where can we pee?"

Simon pointed. "We use that corner. And there's a box for sittin'." We looked around, barely making out the corner of the room that Simon had pointed out.

"Simon," I asked, "do you have anything to eat?"

"Yes," he replied. "This is our fire here. That's his over there." We could see a faint glow reflecting off a facing of rock on the far side of the cabin.

"Son," said Mrs. Murphy from her bed, "stir up the ashes and see if you can get some fire."

"We don't have any more wood. He gets mad when I ask for it."

"I'll get it." Frances crept towards the light of the fire. Finding some small sticks of wood, she pulled a few with her, a little at a time, backing towards us.

Simon stirred the ashes and found a tiny coal. He blew on it, feeding it slivers of wood until curls of gray smoke began showing and then yellow flames started the wood crackling. We held our hands out to the fire, glad for its cheery presence.

The misery there, in that dank cabin, went on for several days. We slept and woke, hardly aware of anything. Mrs. Murphy felt a grandmotherly concern, and was kindly, but could do little.

We were frightened of Mr. Keseberg, who did not want to be bothered with three wet, cold, whimpering children who cried constantly for their mother. To us, he seemed like a ghoulish giant, looming suddenly over us when our crying annoyed him. "Stop your sniveling! There's nothing that can be done for you!"

One morning, as we huddled together, we were startled awake by someone close to us, touching us. We began to whimper and crawled away from the touch, clinging to each other.

"Hush, hush, it's all right." It was Mother! She gathered us into her arms.

"Who is there?" The weak voice of Mrs. Murphy cried out. "Is it men from California?"

We were clinging to Mother and she had trouble getting to her feet, but managed to move closer to Mrs. Murphy. "It's Tamsen Donner."

"Oh, Tamsen," said Mrs. Murphy. "Thank God you're here. I cain't do anythin' for the little ones. I cain't move about."

Mr. Keseberg limped toward us, bending over to peer at Mother. "Ahh. Mrs. Donner. Those men they leave the *kinder* here."

"Mr. Keseberg, we will go to the other cabin."

"That cabin is empty. The Breen's have gone."

"Yes. Do you have something I can carry some coals in? I need to build a fire."

"*Ja.* I think so."

Mrs. Murphy held a trembling hand out to Mother. "Don't go away."

"I will be close by, at the other cabin."

The snow was very high, but we followed a path through the mounds. Mother had a hard time pulling the door of the cabin open as snow had drifted against it. It was dim and cold inside. There was a pile of firewood near the fireplace and Mother made a fire with the coals Mr. Keseberg had given her.

"Girls, let's get those wet clothes off. Mr. Clark killed a bear cub. I've brought meat for you."

She bundled us up in a quilt that had been left in the cabin. We sat as close to the fire as we could get, eating the meat and drinking tea from china cups that Mrs. Breen had left on a shelf in the cabin.

We spread our clothes out before the fire to dry, and then snuggled close. We asked about Father and the others in our camp. "Father is very weak. Juan Baptiste and Mr. Clark are to stay with him. I grieve to tell you, but Aunt Betsey and the two little ones have died."

I thought of my cousins, and Aunt Betsey. Now so strange to us and not like they had been back home. I began to cry and my sisters did too.

"I am sad for them too," said Mother.

At daylight Mother made tea. "We're going back to our camp, but I need to get your clothes dry."

"I'm hungry. Do you have any more food?"

"No, Georgia, I'm sorry."

"Can you go to the other cabin and get some? Simon gets meat from the dead bodies and cooks it for us," said Frances.

"I do not want to go there again. I feel very sorry for Mrs. Murphy but I can do nothing for her. I would feel compelled to stay with her. I must get back to Father."

We were preparing to leave when we heard a faint shout from outside the cabin.

"Halloo, the cabin!" We pushed open the door and were surprised to see a group of men and with them was Juan Baptiste.

"Baptiste!" cried Mother. "You were to stay with Mr. Donner. Is he ... ?"

"*Señora* Tamsen, he was the same. I am afraid to stay in these mountains longer, so I leave with Clark. We go the other side of this lake to the foot of the mountain pass, but Clark is very tired because of the pack of things he carry. We camp there last night." Baptiste waved in the direction of four men. "This morning I see Eddy and Foster, and the others, an' I come with them."

We recognized Mr. Miller. "Oh, Hiram, you didn't go out?" Mother said to him.

"No, ma'am, we met these men as they were coming up an' I decided to come back to help. This here's Thompson," he said, pointing to the last man.

"Mrs. Donner," said Eddy, "we must hurry on. My son, and Will's son, were left in the care of Mrs. Murphy. We were told they were still alive."

"They've not survived, Mr. Eddy," said Mother.

Mr. Eddy turned away, stricken.

"Did you say my son is dead?" asked Mr. Foster.

"Yes, I'm sorry."

The men hurried off toward the Murphy cabin. Shortly they came back with Simon, helping him struggle through the snow.

"We can do nothing for Mrs. Murphy. I fear she will die shortly. Keseberg is too weak and lame to walk. We will have to leave them here. I've left what food we can spare. We will take you and your girls and Simon. We must leave soon."

Mr. Eddy took some biscuits and dried beef from his pack and we sat down on a log to eat.

"Mrs. Donner," said Mr. Eddy, "it does not seem reasonable for you to return to your camp."

"Can you delay long enough for me to return to my husband and see if—"

"We cannot stay. We fear another storm will come before we can reach the lower mountains."

Mother looked away, standing very still for a few moments. Then she turned to us.

"Girls, Mr. Eddy and the other men are going to carry you over the mountains. Be good girls and do what they tell you."

"Mother, no." We began to cry. "We want to stay with you."

"Everything will be all right. Think about how nice it will be in the new country. It will be green and warm and there'll be plenty of good food. Father and I will come soon."

"Mrs. Donner," said Mr. Eddy, "I implore you to leave with us."

"Mr. Eddy, promise me that you will watch over my little ones and get them safely to Mr. Sutter. I will give you money."

"I will do my best. All that is within my power, but I will take no money."

He looked away as tears began running down his face. "I tried to save my children. We could have gotten help earlier if only we hadn't become lost in the mountains." His sentence ended in a groan.

"You went out with the group that left just before Christmas?"

He sighed dejectedly and began to tie up his pack. "We were dogged by misfortune and bad luck. Only seven of the fifteen survived. It was a *month* we struggled in the snow."

"Is there another party coming soon?"

"I can't say. It will be June before the snow melts enough so horses can get over the mountain. Some of the others will be coming back to get the things they have cached." He stood up and hefted his pack onto his back, signaling to the other men.

Tears were streaming down Baptiste's face. *"Adios, Señora. Te espero ver otra vez. Vaya con Dios."*

"And God be with you too, Baptiste." Mother clutched us to her one more time, then turned and hurried away.

Frances and Simon were helped along by Mr. Foster, Mr. Eddy took Georgia, and Mr. Miller put me in a blanket and hefted me onto his back. Juan Baptiste helped us as best he could, but he was weak and straggled behind at times. When we reached the head of the lake the men stopped for the night.

Mr. Thompson had noticed the trouble Frances was having with her shoes. "Lassie, we need to do somethin' about your shoes." He turned the shoes around in his hands and shook his head. He tried filling the back of the shoes with some leather he cut off his jacket, but the shoes still slipped off her feet. Then he took a pair of gloves and fashioned some moccasins, filling the inside with wool cloth he cut off a blanket.

We started again at first light. It was a steep climb, treacherous with slippery rock and snow-covered crevices. Near the end of the day Mr. Miller told me he was very tired from carrying me, and enticed me to walk with a promise of a treat of a lump of sugar.

"Little girl, do you see that burned tree up there?" He pointed to black speck way up on a ridge. "You'll only have to walk to there."

I was glad to be put down because my arms and legs were sore from thumping against Mr. Miller's back. I stumbled and sank to my knees time after time, but pressed doggedly on, thinking of my reward. After supper, I asked for the sugar.

"Little girl, we don't have any sugar. I just tol' you that story so's

you'd walk. Now hush about it."

The disappointment was bitter. Huddled together with my sisters, I cried until I fell asleep exhausted. The next day, when Mr. Miller told me that I must walk again, I refused to go forward and cried to go back.

"Look, little girl, you're gonna haf' to walk. If'n you don't want to, you can stay here on the snow an' cry. I saw a big bear snuffling around the camp last night an' he might come an' eat you."

I cried even harder, and sat down in the snow. Mr. Miller pulled me up, but I refused to stand. He started off, saying he would leave me. This frightened Frances and Georgia and they tried to get me up.

"We can't go back. Come on, we'll help you."

"I don't like that man. He's mean."

Frances and Georgia began to cry too, fearing that I would be left behind. Then the other men came back and spoke heatedly with Mr. Miller and once again he put me on his back and the journey continued.

At one point the men picked up a bundle lying on the snow, and

Frances recognized it as the bag of keepsakes and clothing that Mother had entrusted to Mr. Cady and Mr. Stone.

As we proceeded we saw other people, rescuers and rescued, moving down from the mountains. It was after dark when we reached country that was below the snow line. We remained several days at Mule Springs, glorying in the warm dry earth and a view of green fields.

We were taken across the river in an Indian canoe and followed a path through the marshes to Sutter's Fort. Our half-sisters welcomed us with open arms.

Chapter Thirteen

We were safe, but Mother and Father were still in the mountains.

Elitha and Leanna had prepared as best they could for the time when we would all be brought down from the mountains. The room in which they were staying when we arrived at Sutter's Fort was part of a crude adobe structure outside the walls of the fort. We little ones were oblivious to discomfort, relishing our safe surroundings, but each day watching the road that we might see Father and Mother brought down from the mountains. It was not to be.

We were too young to comprehend the dark clouds that were still in our future. Frances was barely seven, Georgia five, and I, four. Elitha told me, years later, of that time. *"After Leanna and I reached the Fort with the first relief, we were put in different families to await our parents, but as soon as the Second Relief was expected, we went to housekeeping, gathered wood, and had everything ready. No one came. Then we waited and watched anxiously for the third relief, and it was a sad sight to see you three and no more. Sister Leanna and I talked long after you three were asleep, wondering what we should do. You had no clothes, except those you wore, so the next day I got a little cotton stuff and commenced making you some. Leanna did the cooking and looked after you, which took all her time."*

Another rescue group was organized to go to those left in the mountains, but was stopped because of the rapidly melting snow. In mid-April, a party made their way to the mountains, and returned in May with horses laden with packs of goods. We learned that our Mother and Father were dead. Only Mr. Keseberg remained alive.

We were desolate. The people of the community around the fort were sympathetic, but we soon fled from the pity. Leanna and Elitha were very young, Elitha, fourteen, and Leanna, twelve. The responsibility for caring for three little ones was crushing. The property of our parents was sold at auction, and half the proceeds given to the leader of the fourth rescue party, Mr. Fallon. The money was put in the hands of an appointed guardian, but was not made available to us, and our situation became desperate.

The clothing that Elitha had made for us was stolen as it dried on a line, and once again we were destitute of clothing. Georgia described this situation in one of her letters.

... there was a time while at the Fort that you and I had not but a worn out calico dress to guard us from the cold. Frances was fortunate to own one garment besides a dress. Perhaps you do not remember the pantalet she made for you with skill that would have been a credit to an older person. She sewed the different sized pieces of several colors together, and every time that a little scrap had been added you obeyed good-naturedly her command to try it on. We three gazed at it admiringly when it was wide enough to slip on and tied with a string below your knee.

For a time, Elitha and Leanna were employed in separate households, and given food as payment. It was not enough and sometimes we were hungry. We wandered the village, sometimes finding our way to the Indian village. The Indian mothers were kind to us, giving us dried fish and acorn meal to eat. Many times we would creep to a dark corner to cry, the pain of missing Mother and Father more than we could bear.

One June evening, we could not find our sisters. A woman came to us and told us that we should spend the night with her, and the next day she took us to another house where people had gathered. There we saw Leanna and Elitha. We learned that Elitha was now the wife of Mr. Perry McCoon and was going to live on his ranch. She left with a promise that soon we would join them. We were assured that peace and happiness would come to us at last. And so we waited, staying here and there, until one day we met a little old woman on the road.

"Grüst euch, Kleine Mädels ich habe euch etwas gebracht," she said to us, but of course we couldn't understand her.

"Good morning, Grandma," we said, greeting her with a title we had been taught to use when speaking to old people. She had with her a tin pail that held bread, butter and cheese, and it was for us!

The lady, whose name was Mrs. Brunner, agreed to take Georgia and me into her home on the condition that Leanna would come to help with the work of having us. So Georgia and I, and Leanna, were together, but Frances was taken somewhere else. It would be five years before we would see her again.

Mrs. Brunner could understand English better than she could speak it. She and Christian Brunner, her husband, and Jacob, her brother-in-law, had come from a place far-away across lands and big waters where most of the people spoke both French and German.

Not too long after we went to Mrs. Brunner, Elitha and her husband came to get us. I was the only sister that would go with her, lured away from Georgia with the promise of my own pony that I could ride back to visit any time I wished. That promise turned out not to be true.

Life on the McCoon ranch was good. There were many Indians working on the ranch, and I acquired an Indian friend named Billy. But then, Mr. McCoon took Elitha away to San Francisco, and left me in the care of Mr. and Mrs. Packwood. I became lonely, thinking more and more of my sisters and the folks at Grandma's house, and longed for them. Many times I would hide to feel sorry for myself, for I had been taught not to be a cry-baby, or people would not like me.

Then, unexpectedly, Georgia and Leanna came to visit. Words cannot express my joy, and then my dismay, when early the next morning I saw them leaving. I ran after them, but was brought back. I could not be consoled. It took a long time for me to return to good spirits.

The leaves fell, and the nights became frosty. One day Mr. McCoon brought my sister back to the ranch, and we enjoyed some happy times together, but in the spring of 1848 my brother-in-law told me that Grandma Brunner was preparing to move to Sonoma and she'd sent word that she would like for me to go to her. I tied my few things in a handkerchief, Mr. McCoon lifted me onto a pony and took me to people who were going to Sonoma.

The Brunners had established a dairy on their farm and Mr. Brunner had a butcher shop in town. Georgia and I spent many happy hours, and learned some of our hardest lessons, with the Brunners. We were assigned numerous chores and tasks.

Leanna became lonely for Elitha, and decided to go to live with her. When she collected her things to go away, she gave us a pair of black silk stockings which had been knit by our own dear mother. They were marked near the top in fine cross-stitch in white with a "D", and under that with a "5".

These were our only keepsakes, until one day we spied, on a high shelf, the little tin box that Mother had carried across the country, and we had last seen at our mountain camp. Now, instead of the papers and keepsakes we knew so well, it contained sugar. We felt it was too sacred for us ever to have for our own, but one day we found it thrown away, one side unsoldered and the bottom hanging loose.

How I wish now that we could have known how Grandma Brunner came into possession of it. We kept the treasure where we could see it often, and years later it was repaired and I cherish it still.

The Brunners became very fond of us, and we reciprocated in that

feeling as they were then our family. Grandma wanted us to become what she referred to as *"Schweitzer* children". We were dressed in clothing like Grandma wore as a small child, and we learned to speak German. Grandma did not like it when we spoke our own language.

There was more than a passing interest in Georgia and me within the little community in which we now lived, for the stories of the sufferings of the Donner Party had been carried to all the settlements and to many parts of the United States. Some of these stories would be told in our presence and were cruel to hear.

In 1848, the cry of "Gold! resounded throughout the territory, and the free-spending miners caused an increase in Grandma's business. Our days were filled with chores of all kinds, but there were also times when we participated in social events.

We had meshed into this life, and when Governor Boggs came one day with a letter from our auntie, Elizabeth Poor, begging that we three little orphans be sent to her in Massachusetts, Grandma refused to give us up.

Governor Boggs explained that we would have opportunity for

schooling, and we would benefit in many ways, but to no effect. He promised to send word to our aunt that we were situated nicely.

We were sad, as Mother had taught us to love Aunty Poor, and we wished that we could visit with her. I determined that I would learn to write as fast as I could, so that I could send her a letter about us.

One day we happened to be home alone when we saw a bareback rider tie up his horse by the kitchen door, and we realized it was Juan Baptiste. After greeting us with affection, he took a brown paper parcel from his pocket, giving to us the contents; two bunches of the most beautiful raisins we had ever seen.

He told us that he wanted to soften our recollections of the hard times in the mountains and that he had promised our mother to try to keep us in sight and to do what he could for us. He was gone when Grandma returned, and she was distressed when she learned of his visit. She rarely spoke to us of our mother, fearing it would lessen our affection for herself.

Fall came and Grandma made arrangements for us to attend the first American school in Sonoma, in exchange for some of her dairy produce, but our attendance was brief. Grandma felt we could be instructed well enough at home, and she needed us to help with the work on the farm.

Grandma Brunner was well versed in the healing arts, and when a time came that many of the fellows who had left for the gold fields, happy and full of health and enthusiasm, returned broken and sick. As a result, we became well acquainted with many as we were needed to help Grandma as she tended to them.

Our presence sometimes caused their thoughts to turn to home and family back in the States, but many times their thoughts and discussion would turn to our disaster in the snow-bound camps.

The newspaper, *The California Star*, had carried sensationalized articles, casting the ordeal in the mountains in a horrible and cruel way. The tales were false; we were convinced of that, but they wounded never the less and we suffered crying spells over what we heard.

These unhappy moments caused a deep fire within me to someday dispel the malicious rumors that abounded about what had happened in the mountain camps.

In 1850, we received a letter from Elitha bearing the sad news that her husband had been thrown from his horse and killed, and that her little daughter and our sister Leanna were now with her on the ranch.

During our years with the Brunners, Elitha kept in contact, but Grandma, fearful that she would lose us, rejected the overtures that were made. Then in the summer of 1852 we received a letter from Frances who'd been living all these years with Mr. and Mrs. Reed.

I am happy, but there has not been a day since I left Sutter's fort that I haven't thought of my little sisters and wanted to see them.

Hiram Miller, our guardian, says he will take me to see you soon, and Elitha is going too.

I remembered Mr. Miller, and dreaded his coming for I had not forgotten his harsh treatment of me in the mountains.

It was autumn when they came. Elitha, well-dressed, tall and slender; Leanna, now thirteen, appearing completely new to us except for the same blue eyes and fair hair. We learned that Leanna was to be married and was going to a home of her own, and that Frances was now going to live with Elitha.

Mr. Miller spent very little time with us, except for a serious talk with Grandma, when he asked her the amount that was due to her for the trouble and expense of taking us into her home. Grandma was indignant, replying that we were now her children and nothing was due. Grandma's answer discouraged Elitha's hopes that we sisters could once again be united in one home.

As the years went on, Grandma Brunner became easily offended and upset with any indication that we were longing for our family, or forming our own opinions about our upbringing and our surroundings. We became more and more rebellious because we felt the incidents that caused Grandma to be upset and angry were not of our making.

Georgia went to a neighbor, staying for quite awhile. When she returned, she was speaking English instead of German. This angered Grandma and she threatened to send Georgia to live with strangers, but soon realized she was likely to lose both of us as we would not stand to be separated. For awhile she became easier on us, permitting us to attend school and sometimes Sunday school too.

We were visited by Elitha and her new husband, Mr. Benjamin Wilder, who supported her efforts to take us into their home, but to no avail.

I was eleven and Georgia twelve, when an incident of such unfairness occurred that we determined we would leave the Brunner household. By that time we had the will to stand up for what was right for us. A visitor, a lady from Grandma's own far-off country, came to visit, determined to convince Grandma that Georgia and I were not deserving of being Grandma's children, and beneficiaries of her property.

She wanted Grandma to take *her* children as heirs. The lady, Mrs. Stein, had filled Grandma's ears with distortions of all that she had questioned me about Grandma's affairs and my family.

In a rage, Grandma called me before the visitors and others. I do not know how I got into the room. Her tirade against me cut into my heart, and to this day, I remember every hurtful word.

"ich habe sie aufgenommen als sie am verhungern war, habe sie aufgezogen bis sie fast so gross war wie ich. Ich schenkte ihr meine Liebe und mein Vertrauen, alles was sie weiss hat sie von mir gelernt. Das Heim, das sie beschützt hat. hat sie verdüstert, die Hand, die sie ernährt hat, hat sie verletzt; sie ist der Liebe die man ihr schenkte total unwürdig."

I fled out of the house, into the dark to the old bent tree where I had gone so many times before in times of trouble. I stretched my arms toward heaven, and cried out. "She said I have blackened her home! Wounded the hand that has fed me, unworthy of the love given to me! Oh, God, I'm all alone—please, take care of me!"

After a while I became calm, and began to plan. Georgia and I would leave Sonoma.

My chores were finished the next morning before Grandma called me to her. "On account of your bad conduct, Mrs. Stein is going to shorten her stay, and I am going with her. She says that she has kept back the worst things that you have told about me, but will tell them to me on the road."

Indignant, I defended myself. "I have not been false to you. I promise to stay and take care of everything while you go and hear what more she has to tell, but after the home-coming, I leave. I am thankful for the home I have had, but will not be a burden to you longer."

Grandma returned, having determined that Mrs. Stein had told her lies, and found that Elitha and her husband were in Sonoma, that Georgia was with them, and that I would leave the next morning.

I knew it would be hard for both of us, for dear, childish Grandma was ready to forgive and forget. I, however, smarting under the wrong and injustice that had been done to me, felt she had nothing to forgive. I took care to keep from Grandpa's sight, for I knew that he would miss me, and I could not bear to say the parting words.

We left Sonoma with Elitha and Benjamin, excited and apprehensive that somehow Grandma would manage to keep us from leaving, but it didn't happen.

On reaching the ferry across the Sacramento River, I was astonished at the changes of seven and a half years. The river was crowded with commerce, and the tule flat between the waterfront and Sutter's Fort had become a city. We arrived at the white house on K Street and greeted our sister, Frances, with joyful tears. For the first time since leaving the mountains we five sisters were together. We were grateful for our new home, and immediately blended into the household. The first Monday in October, we three younger sisters set off together to go to school.

The change of circumstances did not lessen the grateful and caring thoughts of the couple that gave us a home when we were little orphan waifs. Finally I decided to write to them and after some weeks I received a reply.

Dear Eliza:

Your letter of the fifteenth of June came duly to hand, giving me great satisfaction in regard to your health, as well as keeping me and grandfather in good memory ... I am glad to learn that you enjoy a country life. We have sold lately twelve cows, and are milking fifteen at present. You want to know how Flower is coming on: had you not better come and see for yourself? Hard feelings or ill will we have none against you; and why should I not forgive little troubles that are past and gone by? The roses you planted on Jacob's grave are growing beautifully, and our garden looks well. Grandfather and myself enjoy good health, and we wish you the same for all time to come. We give you our love, and remain, in parental affection,

Mary and Christian Brunner.

Many years later, with my husband, Sherman Houghton, I returned to the place where I had spent most of my growing years. It was a joyful but also a sad reunion with Grandma and Grandpa, now frail and beset with many problems.

We five Donner sisters went on to happy, fulfilling lives, but were forever haunted by the events in the mountains. From the beginning we were reluctant to talk of what happened because of the coarse and brutal way the entrapment was depicted in the accounts of the time. Facts were interwoven with wild rumor and the brutal stories published in *The California Star* newspaper later became the basis for accounts that added even more untruths.

The people of the Donner Party did all they could to save themselves from their terrible prison in the snow. They tried to break through the deep snow on the mountain and failed; fished, and caught nothing; hunted and found little; ate the glue from boiled hides, and found no nutrition. It is a testament to faith and determination that forty-five of the eighty-one who were trapped in the mountains survived.

I have always believed that no one was to blame for the misfortunes which overtook us in the mountains. The dangers and difficulties encountered by reason of taking the Hastings Cut-off had all been surmounted—two weeks more and we should have reached our destination in safety.

I have not been back to those mountains, but someday I will go. Someday, when I can bear it, I will find the place of those miserable camps, and I will walk the ground over the remains of my mother and father, uncle and aunt, and the others who perished there.

I will carry with me wildflowers, and I will scatter them over the ground. If you, my reader, should visit there, would you do the same?

THE PEOPLE OF THE DONNER PARTY
(Bold type signifies those who survived the ordeal.)

DONNER AND REED FAMILIES

George Donner, 62

      Tamsen Eustis Donner, 45

      Elitha Donner, 14

      Leanna Donner, 12

      Frances Donner, 6

      Georgeanna Donner, 4

      Eliza Donner, 3

Jacob Donner, 59

      Elizabeth Donner, 45

      Solomon Hook, 14

      William Hook, 12

      George Donner Jr., 9

      Mary Donner, 7

      Isaac Donner, 5

      Samuel Donner, 4

      Lewis Donner, 3

      Noah James, 20 Employee

      Samuel Shoemaker, 25 Employee

      John Denton, 28 Employee

James Reed, 45

      Margaret Reed, 32

      Virginia Backenstoe Reed, 13

      Martha (Patty) Reed, 9

      James Reed Jr. 5

      Thomas Reed, 3

      Mrs. Keyes, 73, Margaret's mother

      Eliza Williams, 31 Employee

      Baylis Williams, 24 Employee

      Milford Elliott, 28 Employee

      Walter Herron, 25 Employee

      James Smith, 25 Employee

OTHER MEMBERS

Luke Halloran, 25

Charles Stanton, 35

Patrick Breen, 51

Margaret Breen, 40

John Breen, 14

Edward Breen, 13

Patrick Breen Jr., 11

Simon Breen, 9

Peter Breen, 7

James Breen, 5

Isabella Breen, infant

Patrick Dolan, 30

William Eddy, 28

Eleanor Eddy, 25

James Eddy, 3

Margaret Eddy, 1

Levineh Murphy, 36, Widow

Landrum Murphy, 16

Mary Murphy, 14

Lemuel Murphy, 12

William G. Murphy, 10

Simon P. Murphy, 8

Sarah Murphy Foster, 19

William M. Foster, 30

George Foster, 4

Harriet Murphy Pike, 18

William M. Pike, 25, Harriet's husband

Naomi Pike, 3

Catherine Pike, 1

Lewis Keseberg, 32

Philippine Keseberg, 23

Ada Keseberg, 3
Lewis Keseberg Jr., infant
Jacob Wolfinger, 26
Doris Wolfinger, 19
Karl Burger, 30 (Dutch Charley)
Augustus Spitzer, 30
Joseph Reinhardt, 30
Mr. Hardcoop, 60
William McCutcheon, 30
    Amanda McCutcheon, 30
    Harriet McCutcheon, infant
Franklin Ward Graves, 57
    Elizabeth Cooper Graves, 45
    Mary Ann Graves, 19
    William C. Graves, 17
    Eleanor Graves, 14
    Lovina Graves, 12
    Nancy Graves, 8
    Jonathan B. Graves, 7
    Franklin Ward Graves Jr., 5
    Elizabeth Graves, infant
    Sarah Fosdick Graves, 21
    Jay Fosdick, 23, husband of Sarah
    John Snyder, 25 Teamster
John Baptiste Trudeau, 16
Antoine, 23
Luis, 19, *Miwok Indian*
Salvador, 28, *Miwok Indians*

RESCUERS MENTIONED

Charles L. Cady
Nicholas Clark

William O. Fallon
Charles Stone
John Stark
Reason Tucker
William Thompson
John Rhodes

OTHER REAL PEOPLE ON THE TRAIL
Edwin Bryant
Lilburn Boggs
Jim Bridger
James Clyman
Reverend Cornwall
Reverend and Mrs. Dunleavy
Mrs. Dunbar
Charles Frémont
Miles Goodyear
Colonel "Owl" Russell
William Sublette
Nancy and J. Quinn Thornton
Luis Vasquez
Jim Bridger
Joseph Walker
Old Bill Williams

FICTIONAL CHARACTERS
Zeb, the old mountain man
Mr. New, mountain man.
Blue Whirlwind, Indian healer.
Little Elk
Mr. Tibbets, owner of the mule. (Story is true.)
Jim, the mountain man. (Story is true.)

LIST OF SOURCES

Acuff, Marilyn. Keseberg family history.

Angier, Bradford. Stackpole Books, 1978. *Field Guide to Medicinal Wild Plants*.

Askenasy, Hans. *Cannibalism, From Sacrifice to Survival*. Prometheum Books, New York, 1994.

Bancroft, Hubert. *History of California,* Vol. Five, 1846-1848.

Bornali, Halder. Article: *Lakota Sioux Plant and Stone Symbolism*. LakotaArchives.com.

Breen, Patrick, *Diary*. Manuscript in Bancroft Library,
Brown, Dee. *The Gentle Tamers*. University of Nebraska Press, 1958.

Bryant, Edwin. *What I Saw in California*. University of Nebraska Press, 1985.

Clyman, James. *Journal of a Mountain Man*. Tamarack Books, Boise, Idaho.

Curran, Harold. *Fearful Crossing. The Central Overland Trail Through Nevada*. Nevada Publications, originally published in 1982.

Davis, William C. *Frontier Skills, The Tactics and Weapons that Won the American West*. The Lyons Press, Guilford, Conn., 2003.

Devoto, Bernard. *The Year of Decision 1846*. Little, Brown and Company, 1943.

Donner, Tamsen. *Letter,* May 11, 1846, Huntington Library.

Donner, Tamsen. *Letter, June 16, 1846*. Springfield Journal, July 30, 1846.

Donovan, Lewis. Pioneers of California, *True Stories of Early Settlers in the Golden State*. Scottwall Associates, 1993.

Durham, Michael S. *Desert Between the Mountains,* Henry Holt & Company

Egan, Ferol. *Fremont, Explorer For A Restless Nation*. University of Nevada Press. Orig. published by Doubleday, 1977.

Farnham, Eliza. *Narrative of the Emigration of the Donner Party to California in 1846*. California Indoors and Out. New York, 1856.

Fiddyment Family Archives *Letter, Georgia Babcock to Eliza Houghton, 1894*

Graves, William C. *"Crossing the Plains in '46,"* The Russian River Flag (Healdsburg).

Graydon, Charles K. *Trail of the First Wagons Over the Sierra Nevada.* The Patrice Press, Tucson, Arizona, 1986.

Hardesty, Donald L. *The Archaeology of the Donner Party.* University of Nevada Press, Reno, Nevada, 1997.

Harlan, Jacob Wright. *California, '36 to '48.* The Bancroft Company, 1888.

Hassrick, Royal B. *The Sioux, Life and Customs of a Warrior Society.* University of Oklahoma Press, 1964.

Houghton, Eliza P. Donner. *The Expedition of the Donner Party and Its Tragic Fate.* A.C. McClurg & Co., 1911

Johnson, Kristin. *"Unfortunate Emigrants" Narratives of the Donner Party.* Utah State University Press, Logan, Utah, 1996.

Johnson, Kristin. Article: *Tamsen's Other Children.* Donner Party Bulletin, September/October 1997.

Kelly, Charles. *Salt Desert Trails.* Western Epics, Inc., Salt Lake City, Utah.

King, Joseph A. *A New Look at the Donner Party,* K & K Publications, 1992.

Korns, J. Roderic & Morgan, Dale, Ed. *West From For Bridger 1846-1850.* Utah State University Press, Logan, Utah, 1994.

Laycock, George. *The Mountain Men.* The Lyons Press, Guilford, Conn., 1988.

Lockley, Fred. *Conversations with Pioneer Women.* Rainy Day Press, Eugene, Oregon, 1981.

Lavender, David. *Bent's Fort.* University of Nebraska Press.

Luchetti, Cathy and Olwell, Carol. *Women of the West.* The Library of the American West. Orion Books.

Marcy, Randolph B. *The Prairie Traveler.* Applewood Books.

McGlashan, C.F. *History of the Donner Party.* A.L. Bancroft Company, 1880.

Morgan, Dale Ed. *Overland in 1846: Diaries and Letters of the California-Oregon Trail.* University of Nebraska Press.

Mullen, Frank Jr. *The Donner Party Chronicles.* Nevada Humanities Committee, 1997.

Munkres, Robert L. *People & Places on the Road West.* New Concord Press, 2003.

Murphy, Virginia Reed. *Across the Plains in the Donner Party.* Outbooks, 1980.

Myres, Sandra L. *Westering Women and the Frontier Experience, 1800-1915.* University of New Mexico Press.

Peterson, Lee Allen. *A Field Guide to Edible Wild Plants.* Houghton Mifflin Company, New York, 1977.

Pringle, Lawrence. *Wild Foods,* Four Winds Press.

Reed, James Frazier. *"From a California Emigrant,* Sangamo Journal (Springfield). November 5, 1846.

Reed, James Frazier. *"Narrative of the Sufferings of a Company of Emigrants in the Mountains of California, in the Winter of '46 & '47."* Illinois Journal (Springfield).

Reed, James Frazier. *"The Snow-Bound, Starved Emigrants of 1846."* Pacific Rural Press.

Reed, James Frazier. *Letter,* May 20, 1846. Transcribed by Kristin Johnson, published by the Utah Crossroads Chapter of the Oregon-California Trails Association.

Schlissel, Lillian. *Women's Diaries of the Westward Journey.* Schoken Books, 1982.

Schmidt, JoAnne. Donner family genealogy.

Stewart, George. *Ordeal By Hunger.* Henry Holt & Co., 1936.

The Gaps Index, *Listing of Old Disease Names and their Modern Definitions.* Genetic Information and Patient Services, Inc. (GAPS).

Thornton, Jessie Quinn. *Camp of Death: The Donner Party*

Mountain Camp 1846-47. Harper & Brothers, New York, 1849.

Tilford, Gregory L. *Edible and Medicinal Plants of the West.* Mountain Press Publishing Co., 1997.

Whitman, Narcissa Prentiss. *My Journal, 1836.* Ye Galleon Press, Fairfield, Washington, 2002

ILLUSTRATION CREDITS

The Bancroft Library, Pages 179 & 223, *Patty Reed visits the site of the entrapment.*

The Emigrant Trail Museum, Truckee, Calif., Pages 151, 128

Joslyn Art Museum, Omaha, Nebraska, Page 58.

Roy Kerswill, Pages 11, 35, 37, 115, 165; Adaptations, Pages 1, 69, 71, 85, 101, 103, 113, 201, 213.

Diana Monfalcone, Reno, Nevada, Portraits; Eliza Donner (in the forward section of book) and Mrs. Brunner with Eliza and Georgia Donner, Page 217.

Gilcrease Museum, Tulsa, Oklahoma, *Page 53.*

Scotts Bluff National Monument, Gering, Nebraska, The art of William Henry Jackson, Pages 9-*Westport Landing,* 42-*Approaching Chimney Rock,* 54-*Rendezvous..*

Sutters Fort, Sacramento, Calif. *Sutters Fort in 1846,* Page 211, 213.

Wyoming Division of Cultural Resources, *Ft. Bridger,* Page 87.

Author's Collection, Pages 131, 133, 147, 149, 181, 199, 201, 209, 213.

Author Frankye Craig became interested in the Donner Party saga while developing a sesquicentennial event at Donner Memorial State Park in 1996.

Since then she has become one of a number of people active in Donner Party history and has been interviewed several times for television programs.

She has also put together a series of Donner Party events, including several cross-country tours.

Frankye resides in Reno, Nevada. She is also the author of *The Fateful Journey of Tamsen Donner,* published in April, 2006.

Web site: www.donnerpartyhistory.com